Saving Grace

Saving Grace

JENNIFER BANKS

POOLBEG

Published 2006
by Poolbeg Press Ltd
123 Grange Hill, Baldoyle
Dublin 13, Ireland
E-mail: poolbeg@poolbeg.com

© Jennifer Banks 2006

Copyright for typesetting, layout, design
© Poolbeg Press Ltd

The moral right of the author has been asserted.

1 3 5 7 9 10 8 6 4 2

A catalogue record for this book is available from the British Library.

ISBN 1 84223 285-1
ISBN 978-1-84223-285-9 (from Jan 2007)

Typeset by Patricia Hope in Sabon 11.5/15
Printed by Creative Print & Design, Wales

www.poolbeg.com

Acknowledgements

Thanks to:

Dan Dwyer, without whose persistence and guidance I would have lost faith in my ability. My friends and colleagues, Sinéad, Mary, Jackie, Katriona and all at Mediability, for their support and friendship. My GP, Dr Dan Murphy, without whom the past seven years would have been unbearable. My friend and father-in-law Ernest Banks who set me on the road to recovery with his foresight and encouragement – you are and always will be sadly missed. My dear friend, Paddy Doyle, for all the advice and laughter you have brought into my life. Jim Murray whose constant encouragement made the difficult tasks possible. Nicola Carr for listening to me rant and the endless cups of tea and encouragement. Nancy Holland who brought the light back into my life, at a time when I could see only darkness.

For Steve and Keira
Thank you for loving me

Prologue

I married Mehmet in London on the 6th of February 1988. He was the only man who had ever shown me love and affection during my short life, or so it seemed to me at the time. I had had little experience with men in my past other than one short childish romance and some one-night stands in my teens. Mehmet was the first man to say he loved me.

Our wedding had been rushed due to the deportation of Mehmet's friend a few days before. He was caught working illegally on a student visa. Like his friend, Mehmet was Turkish and in England on a student visa. He was also working and at risk of deportation. Not wanting my man to suffer the same fate as his friend, I agreed to marry him a couple of days later, reassured by the fact that he professed his love.

So there I was, sitting in the pub on Brixton Hill with the few guests we could muster, dreaming of what lay ahead. We had been living together, of course, but, nevertheless, like every bride, my head was filled with the fantasy of how my husband and I would make slow passionate love on our wedding night.

During the short walk back to our flat Mehmet was very quiet and seemed distant. I believed he was nervous of what lay ahead and I found this funny. I was so high on love that I didn't even notice how he walked ahead of me, refusing to hold my hand.

Back at the flat I was slightly shaken when he shouted at me to make him tea. Still believing it was nerves, I went about the task as quickly as possible.

I had no sooner put the cup on the table when *Wham!* – Mehmet punched me in the stomach.

Reeling from the shock, I shouted: "What the hell did you do that for?"

"You are my fuckin' wife now – if I ever see you talking to another man I will knife you!"

Whack! – another punch, this time in the face, drawing blood from my nose.

"What the hell are you talking about, you fool?" I cried. "I did nothing wrong!"

"Call *me* a fool you, you fat ugly bitch! No man wants you – I only married you for this damn passport! Until I get it, you will show me the respect I deserve! You are *nothing*, you hear? Now turn off the light and get your clothes off – I don't want to see your ugly fat body!"

"Mehmet, what is wrong? This morning you said you loved me, and now this! Why?"

"Stop crying, you ugly bitch! Get into bed – the least you can do is reward me for marrying you!"

On autopilot I did as I was told, all the while blood and tears running down my face. I could just make out the silhouette of the TV in the corner and, as Mehmet forced me to have sex with him, I kept my eyes on that corner the whole time.

When he had finished with me, he shouted: "Get up, you ugly fat bitch, and shower – then change the bed-sheets! I am not sleeping in a bed stained with the blood of a whore!"

My nose had continued to bleed while he had sex with me.

On my way out the door he kicked me hard in the back – it took every bit of strength in my body to stay standing.

Fearing another beating, I did as I was told, all the while trying not to cry.

Then I went to bed and clenched my fists, waiting for him to sleep so I could get up and cry in the kitchen – alone. It took only a few minutes for him to drop off. I snuck quietly from the bed, trying not to make a sound. I knew I would be beaten again if he woke.

Sitting at the kitchen table, I began to think of all the warnings I had been given about Mehmet. I had lived with him against the wishes of my family. They had met Mehmet once and the mutual hatred was instant – though I think Mam and Dad were put off by his culture before ever meeting him. Whatever their reason, they did not want him in the family and, at that moment on my wedding night, I thought maybe this had played a big part in my decision to marry him. Was I punishing them for not recognising how unwell I was? By marrying a Turkish Muslim, I was ensuring that they would pay attention.

For more than ten years, I had hidden my suffering and pain, and hated my family for not realising how much I hurt, how much I hated my very existence and the utter contempt I felt for myself. Why had no one realised? It was my lack of self-esteem that had allowed Mehmet into my life. He found a woman ready and willing to be controlled. For him it must have seemed easy. A young woman far from home with no one to defend her – he could do whatever he liked and he knew I would take it! I had no way of stopping him and he knew it. I had just been initiated into a whole new chapter of my life. For the past year I had been led slowly to the gates of hell. Tonight I crossed the threshold.

Closing my eyes, I easily slipped back in time to Mammy's kitchen, in the west of Ireland. On the table sat a beautiful happy little girl, with her mother playfully getting her dressed. The love between mother and child filled the room as the mother fluffed the child's hair and arranged the kiss-curl on the forehead, in preparation for the birthday picture. Taking the child's face in her hands, the mother planted a big kiss on her lips and helped her down from the table.

I was the child in the vision: Jennifer Grace Ann.

Now, through my choked tears, I began to wonder how it all went so very wrong.

1

I was born in Salthill, Galway, on the 13th of June 1965, the youngest of nine children: three boys and six girls. I have no memory of ever having a close relationship with my brothers and even now we are distant. But, for my parents and sisters, I was the cute curly-haired kid and commander of attention. For the first four years of my life it was all so perfect.

I am not sure how I remember the kitchen scene. It was my second birthday, and many would believe it impossible to recall such an early event. It may be that the tale was told to me many times by my mother. The resulting photograph took pride of place in our living room, only recently being hung in my own home. Regardless of how the memory was created, it was to bring me comfort throughout my darkest days.

Due to the age gap, I was four when my sisters were in their teens. They were obsessed with dancing and show bands! I had a favourite pastime, much to their annoyance: every weekend I would follow them around as they began the ceremony of preparing for a night out. It was at this time I began to realise the importance of the concept 'thin is beautiful' as bras were stuffed to make breasts appear larger but little or no food was consumed for twenty-four hours before the big night out. There was a craze among the teens during the late sixties for taking laxatives – to lose the extra bulge. My sisters, being totally 'with it' at that time, took laxatives to diminish their imaginary bulges and slim their already sticklike bodies. Lolo (my pet name for Dolores), Mary and Gabrielle ranged from Size 6 to 8 and were little more than 5ft 2 with the tiniest feet. Sandra was a little taller but still stick-thin. Honor, the eldest, was a completely different build: she was tall and slightly larger than the others. I knew she never borrowed their clothes but at the time I just put it down to style. Honor never wore mini-skirts or low-cut tops – she was a blouse and trousers person.

I later went through a phase where I found their preparations for a night out really stupid and believed that they should be locked up. My social life consisted of playing in the street and it was to be a few years yet before I fully understood the concept of looking good.

As I grew older I sometimes wondered why their shoes didn't fit me. The same applied to some of their skirts. I used to try on their clothes when they were at work, hoping the new mini would fit so I could show it off on the street with my friends. But nothing of theirs would fit me though I could have been no more than eight at the time. I was going to be tall and broad, more like Honor, in complete contrast to my petite sisters.

The effect the physical difference between us would

have on my life was profound. Dolores got a new pair of baby-blue trousers once, and I only just managed to force myself into them; even at eight I was much broader than her. The zip broke and I put them back without saying a word. Poor Gabrielle, well known for borrowing Dolores' clothes, was blamed and I watched in silence as the two of them fought. I was too embarrassed to say it was me who broke the zip. How could an eight-year-old child not fit into a pair of trousers belonging to her full-grown sister? I never figured it out. But the memory has always been with me.

But all that was yet to come when, one September morning in 1970, I was told to my utter disgust that I had to go to school that day! And so began an argument with my mother which I was destined to lose. Sitting in the armchair next to the range in the kitchen, I had my arms crossed tightly and refused to move an inch.

"I don't see why I have to go school, Mammy. I will hate it. I want to stay with you!" I cried so much my throat swelled up.

"Every child has to go to school – it's the law. And think of all the new friends you're going to make!"

"I don't care – I am not going – it's a stupid law!"

"You're going whether you like it or not! Now come on and get dressed before I call your father in!"

"I'm only going to run away, you know!"

"Stop your messing and get ready *now!*"

And so it began. I was taken against my will to Scoil Ide primary school in Salthill where I would spend the next nine years of my life. After a few weeks of morning tears and pretend tummy-ache, I settled into the daily routine of attending school, and if I am honest I loved it once I accepted my fate.

It was the getting there and back was the problem.

By the time I reached High Infants, the bully came on the scene. We had to walk the same route to school each day and his taunts began almost immediately after noticing me on the hill one day.

"Hey, fatty! Do you know you have a fat arse?"

"Leave me alone – or I'm going to tell my mother about you!"

"Oh God, I am so scared! Fat Jenny with the jelly-belly and shaky arse, run get your mammy so I can watch you wobble!"

Once I began to cry his taunts got louder. He chased me up the hill laughing and singing his song: *"Jenny on the plate – run and wobble – run and wobble – Jenny on the plate!"*

For five years I was subjected to his taunts.

Along the way an old bat, on the street where I lived, joined in – lying in wait almost every lunch-time to taunt me as I ran home: "Run, fatty, quick! Your dinner is getting cold!"

I have no idea why she did this to me – and never will. Her taunts, combined with the bully's, set in motion the feelings of self-hatred that were to affect my life so much. I was fat and nobody loved me.

I would tell my mum and family about the bullying. They just told me to ignore it. I had hoped that one of my brothers would come to school with me one day. They could show the bullies they couldn't mess with me.

I did ask Brian and John one night at dinner.

"Can one of you take me to school in the morning?"

"Why?"

"I want you to scare the bully. Tell him to leave me alone. Tell him you'll beat him up, if he doesn't stop. Please!"

They laughed. "Don't be stupid! Fight your own battles, you coward!"

This all might have seemed funny to them, but the way I was rejected hurt! I cried in bed that night and vowed I would never forgive any of them.

However, one of the harshest realities I had to face during this time was not the bully or even the old bat; it was the fact that I was no longer important at home. My sister Mary had married and the others, consumed with their love lives and jobs, no longer had time to play with me. I was jealous and hurt as they spent more and more time away from the house. I began to feel that they no longer loved me and, as if to add insult to injury, I had become an aunt! My brother Andy's wife had just given birth to their first child, Michelle – something the kids at school found very funny. None of them had families like mine – they were all close in age to their siblings. I began to believe that I was a freak altogether! I used to run home with the hurt of my travels burning inside, only to find that there was another, more important, drama taking place there. My mother would tell me to wait in the sitting room while the grown-ups talked.

I wanted to scream, "I am hurting! Does anyone care?" but I just went to the washroom and cried.

Our house was always buzzing. In the summer the place was filled with guests as my mother ran a Bed and Breakfast, from Easter through the summer, most of her life. Our house was a large seven-bedroomed, terraced house and my parents had built two chalets in the back garden for us to use during the summer months when the paying guests used our rooms.

My mother was known across the country – her food and hospitality were legendary. "You get the warmest welcome at Maureen McGrath's house!" This was what so many new guests would relay to her after being sent on recommendation to our house.

During the Galway Races it was not unusual to find one of the bookies sleeping in the living room! We had this regular who never booked or arrived on time, yet finding the place full he would beg to stay as he believed his luck at the course depended on it. Mammy always gave in as he knew she would – not for the money but because he was a regular.

It might be difficult to imagine how, in a house filled with young adults and guests, a child could feel so left out, but I did. The cute curly-haired little girl likened to Shirley Temple who would entertain guests with her rendition of 'On The Good Ship Lollipop' for a fifty-pence piece (later spent on *Twinkle* magazine and sweets in Mrs Burke's dusty old sweetshop) was gone. I had outgrown it all and felt like an outsider in my own home. Mammy was always busy, everyone was. I was so convinced that they had forgotten my existence that I believed I was no longer fit to be loved.

My family believed I was a happy child – and at times I was – my life was not always doom and gloom. I have wonderful memories too. I used to go with my mother to visit my grandmother in Ballinasloe. They were special times. It was just my mother and me. I would let my guard down and everything would return to normal. It was mother and daughter once more – the love between us flowed. Away from the others and their problems, I had my mother's full attention and I hated going home to it all again. Strangely, during our times together, I never told Mammy about the bully or how bad I was feeling. I think I was so happy then, I forgot about everything else. Granny used to take me up town and buy me new clothes. I can still remember the navy and white sailor dress with the red bow. I would have my long curls held up in a red satin bow to match the one on the dress. It was the one item of clothing I can vividly remember – in fact I can still feel the excitement of putting it on for the first time.

I looked forward to these visits so much – then my grandmother died. The trips stopped. It was my first experience of death. I never went to the funeral – I was too young – so all I was aware of was that she was gone, never to return.

I also have such happy memories of the times when Aunty Kitty would come down from Dublin every July and look after me while Mammy ran the guesthouse. We had such fun! I can remember giggling in the kitchen as Kitty told my mother in no uncertain terms she was never taking me to the beach again – I would give her heart failure as I swam well beyond my depth. I could swim almost from the first time I set foot in the water. I loved swimming away on Kitty and the fun afterwards in the kitchen when she told Mammy about my adventures, her face still panic-stricken! I sat and listened as I ate my ice cream, knowing that it would happen all over again tomorrow.

But as time went on, it all changed. Was it the bully or

the family? I have no idea. It just happened that I began to keep everything inside – why bother telling people who don't care? Mam was always busy – Maureen McGrath's Guesthouse was never empty in those days. To make matters worse, she had taken this old man from Roscommon in, to live as a permanent guest. He had come for a week and loved it so much he decided to stay. He would sit with us in the evening watching TV when the others were gone out. It should have been just Mam, Dad and me but now we had Tom sitting in the corner by the fire imposing on my time with my parents!

It seemed that all of my mother's time was now taken up by the older people in the house. I used to imagine that they were thieves and would be caught and punished for stealing my mother from me.

Every time I needed help, there was always a more important drama taking place, so I let the pain eat away at my soul instead, knowing my situation could never be as important as the dramas.

"Mam, I need to tell you something."

"Later, I have to sort something out first. You can tell me this evening."

"Fine."

As I was never privy to the 'adult conversations' in the home and I never really knew what the problems were, I invented them. I remember once making up a story that my brother was not my brother at all but an FBI agent and the secret meetings he was having with my parents were actually to keep them informed of his secret missions. As I grew older I learned that smoking, drinking and boyfriends/girlfriends my parents did not approve of were the all-consuming dramas! How disappointing it was to find my imaginary stories were just imaginary!

I clearly remember sitting in my room one day with the anger growing inside me. I had just cried my heart out while an 'adult conversation' was taking place in the kitchen. My brother had just lost another job, it was always something with him. So what? He would find another job. What about me? I wanted to kill myself I was so unhappy. Yet everyone was so consumed with my brother's problems they never noticed mine. He was a married man with a family of his own – why did I have to suffer because of his problems? I thought that you looked after your own life when you married! But no, he had to bring everything to our house and deprive me of the time I so needed with my parents. If only I could have spoken out! But I never did. I just let each minor occurrence build up until I was sure it was my fault for not being good enough. If I sound bitter it is because I was then. I used to get so bloody angry at the lot of them that I could have murdered them. The pain and anger grew ever deeper, the more I was passed over. I wondered if I belonged. If I did, it certainly didn't feel like it.

I had a bully and an old bat at the end of our street telling me how useless I was and all anyone could talk or think about was the others and their stupid problems – none of which were any different to the normal problems teenagers and young adults experience every day in every home in their journey through life.

Why was my home so different? I only wish I knew the answer to this question. No one was on drugs and the only time the police were ever in our home was for a cup of tea and a chat. Mam and Dad, I believe, were overwhelmed by having to deal with young adults in the 60's/70's. In Ireland life was changing and would never be the same again, and they had no idea how to accept this. It is the only reason I can come up with that in some way explains how I was left on the fringes of the family. I was never in trouble. What problems could a little girl possibly have?

I was spoilt in every material way but I would have been so happy if I could have sat down and talked to my family that I would have given every possession away without thought. Inside I was still a little girl needing hugs and kisses but to the outside world my height and size denied my age. At nine, I looked twelve in every way. Maybe because I looked older I was treated as being older. I was lanky and ugly, so who the hell would want to cuddle me? I contemplated suicide all the time. I hated my life – and blamed God for making me this way and my family for not noticing.

Besides all this, I was haunted by the memory of the day I began to believe my mother didn't love me.

I had come in from school – the house seemed dark – I was used to arriving home at lunch-time to blazing fires and a hot lunch. Even if a crisis was taking place, the house itself was always welcoming. Today it was dark.

From upstairs, Daddy called out, "Who is it?"

"It's me – Jennifer! Where's Mammy?"

"Your mother is not very well today!"

Mammy was never sick, never in bed. She was always there in the morning when I woke up and in the evening when I went to sleep. What could be so bad? She didn't get up for breakfast and now she was still in bed at lunch-time! She must be really sick! God, please don't let her die, I prayed as I climbed the stairs.

I entered my parents' bedroom. All I could see was this

gaunt figure in the bed with her blonde hair poking out from under the covers.

"Mammy, what's wrong? What's happened?"

As the covers moved and Mam looked at me, her eyes were blank. "Who are you?"

"It's me, Jennifer. I'm home for lunch."

"I don't know any Jennifer."

At that moment my throat hurt – I wanted to cry.

I'd had a pretty difficult journey home that day. The old bat at the end of the street saw me run home and began shouting: "Run, fatty, or the dinner will get cold!" Some of the other kids on our street had laughed when they heard her.

And now this! My own mother had no idea who I was!

Daddy told me to go down to the kitchen and he would make me some lunch in a minute. I could tell by his eyes he felt my pain but he too was in shock. He had no idea what was wrong with Mammy, with the wife he adored.

I left the room before the tears came.

As I walked down the stairs that day I was a little girl lost. Everyone hated me and now even my own mother had no idea who I was. I believe it was at this moment my life changed completely; the budding feelings of worthlessness and self-hatred had been confirmed. The one person I believed could protect me forever had shown her weakness. This was the first time in my life I had seen her unwell and it scared me so much. I had experienced so much suffering in my short life. Now this. I began to build up defences as I descended the stairs. I had to stop the pain and hurt. I just had no idea how. But I knew I would find a way.

My sisters Honor, Dolores and Gabrielle arrived at the house. A few minutes later my brother John came home. Gabrielle took John and me away until the doctor had been. I had no idea what was happening. The adults decided I was too young to know. The hushed voices and my imagination compounded the whole episode.

Mam recovered in time from whatever was wrong with her but no one told me anything – and it was never explained to me that, after that episode, the doctor put her on Valium, the wonder drug of the 70's and every housewife's friend! With the Valium inside her she became emotionless and I became further detached. For years to come I hoped I could have my mam back the way she used to be – strong, happy and loving. I was too young to understand what was happening. I believed that everything was my fault: if only I wasn't fat none of this would have happened.

In time my body began to change. I was experiencing hormonal changes much earlier than any of my friends and many nights I cried into my pillow as I saw my breasts beginning to stand out and my hips taking on a rounder shape. I used to watch my sisters as they dressed and my body was nothing like theirs – their breasts were actually smaller than mine and my hips were much rounder. How could I be so different to them? We were sisters for God's sake! Why was I not like them?

Mary was a mother by now and I tried once when I was baby-sitting to speak to her about all this. She had come home and was having a cigarette before going to bed. I hoped this quiet moment would lead to a conversation but she just laughed when I began to tell about my feelings. I never bothered trying the others, knowing I would get the same reaction. I had heard them laugh about it before: "Jennifer's puberty will be a hoot!" I was going to talk to Honor about it another time but she was always with Mammy, trying to sort out one of the others.

Honor and Mammy had become allies and together they tried in vain to ensure that the family were always doing the right thing. Mam and Dad were highly respected in the area. I am sure they believed that their children were the only ones causing problems. It was just that no one ever spoke about things back then, and of course it is easy to believe that other people's children are perfect! But of course their parents and mine hid everything, public perception being most important thing! No matter what went on in the home, it stayed in the home – this was the unwritten commandment.

Meanwhile, I became so used to the dramas that I would automatically go to my room or the living room when the kitchen door was closed! I never bothered to let people know I was home most of the time. They would just tell me to go away. So why bother?

I would just appear when the house cleared.

"Hi, Mam."

"Oh, Jennifer, I had no idea you were in."

"Yeah, I just went to my room and started on my homework." The truth was I cried in my pillow for comfort. "What's going on?"

"You should know by now not to ask questions. Adult conversations are private."

"Sure I will find out later when the girls gossip so you may as well tell me."

"Stop the cheek and help me set the table for tea!"

I was so used to this conversation and I am sure I would only ask for pure devilment. I knew that the whispers would begin all over again when Daddy was told about the latest family crisis that night in bed. My father was so quiet and respectable, he would just shake his head and say nothing. It all seems so laughable now that such a minor offence as someone getting drunk or dating an unsuitable person could cause panic in the home. Times have changed to the point of parents now fearing drugs and crime will enter their children's lives, making my family's problems seem so small.

In any case, regardless of the importance of the drama that warranted my parents' full attention, I suffered as a result. I was the forgotten child.

There were only two and a half years between John and me and I used to wish he had been a girl, someone I could talk to. He played football and hung out with the boys and was no use whatsoever when it came to my problems. There was no one I could talk to. I endured the bullying and the self-loathing alone. I used to try and show I was in trouble. I walked around with my head down, my face clearly showing the pain I was in. I realised no one was watching or listening, everyone being consumed with their own problems. With the exception of John, I was in a house full of adults with their own lives. It was fate and timing that took them all away from me, as I was reaching an age of uncertainty and needing support. My sisters and brothers had moved on; no time for the woes of the little sister.

Because I was tall and broad, I thought I was fat as well as ugly. I regularly begged my mother to help me diet yet she was unable to see any reason for this. She tried in vain to reassure me. I was a developing young lady and a diet would stunt my growth. I was really trying to ask for help – maybe I just went about it the wrong way. I don't know but whatever happened my cries went unnoticed. The arguments with my mother escalated.

I muddled through life – tried to ignore the bully and cried later in secret. Sometimes I would hide at the side of the school wall before class to allow the tears to flow. I had friends but never confided in them – after all, I was sure that they really didn't like me! Anyway, what help could they be? None of them could give me what I needed. To be honest I had no idea what I needed, so how could anyone help?

I managed to maintain the appearance of normality. To the people outside my secret world, I seemed to be growing up normally, just like all the rest of my friends, only in my case it was happening a little more quickly.

And so life went on. With hindsight I wonder what would have happened if someone had taken the time to talk to me. But everyone was consumed with his or her life as usual. If I looked happy, then I was happy. No one ever took the time to see beneath the charade. I know if they had, it would have all come out. Maybe then life would have been different.

2

At twelve a virus struck me. I spent a week vomiting and unable to eat. I stood on the old bathroom scales and discovered to my delight I had lost eight pounds. I can still see the blue bathroom with its white walls and royal blue suite – even now I can feel the anticipation as I took the rusty scales from the bottom shelf and laid them on the floor. I knew these scales well, for I would take a deep breath every week before I had the courage to stand on them. Sometimes I rested my hand on the sink to take a few pounds off the result – but today I knew I had no need to do this. I could feel the flesh had melted away during my illness – and I stood on the rusty old scales with pride.

At that very moment I hatched what I believed to be my greatest plan: I could eat my food heartily to hide my secret – then puke out the lot, knowing people would never suspect a thing. Oh God, was I happy! I found it difficult to hide my joy. I was going to lose weight. No one would ever know what I was doing and the bullying would stop.

I felt totally empowered by my fail-proof diet, and my self-confidence appeared to the outsider to increase. I was happily going through life as far as my friends and family were concerned. Just a normal young girl, going through puberty.

By this time I was already having my period and desperately tried to keep my secret from the other girls. I was successful to a point although I was found out to have a sanitary towel in my school bag. I got away with this by telling the girls I took it from my sister's bag and planned to leave it on the teacher's desk. I never did and no further questions were asked. Alone, I shed many tears.

I can remember the day I first sat on the bathroom floor and began the process of purging the food I had consumed. It is not easy to make yourself purge. We have all tried it at some point in our lives. Just try and remember the time you wanted the day off school? It took me ages to purge the first time – in fact I had to give up and try again about three or four times before the vomit came. It's painful and disgusting to make yourself sick – just seeing the vomit alone makes you purge all the more. Maybe I knew deep down my problems had now reached a new height; I had taken a step too far. But the elation of being able to hide my secret overtook any sensible feelings or thoughts I might have had. I was a child and had no real understanding of what I was doing to myself. I hated my life and my body; self-abuse was an almost natural progression for me.

I dearly wish I had never taken this road to

destruction. It was too late when I tried to stop. My eating disorder ruled my life. When I was purging I was happy. If I failed to do it then the whole world came crashing in and I was a no-good failure. I was a sick little girl and purging became my medicine.

At around the same time as my plan was taking shape, Mammy gave in to my cries for help and sent me to see our doctor with a letter. Tired of my talk of wanting to be thin, she believed that this fool of a doctor could put a stop to my complaints and give her head peace. He promptly prescribed another new wonder drug: Iomen! I don't remember him asking any questions. I just told him I wanted to lose weight and he went on about the drug, gave me a prescription and then sent me on my way, warning it would take time for it to work and I had to eat less in order for the drug to do its magic.

When I went home with the slimming pills I told my mother about my conversation with the doctor and her reaction further compounded my feeling of self-loathing.

"The doc gave me these pills – he said they were new to the market and have had great results helping people lose weight."

"There you go then! I told you he'd be able to help, didn't I?"

"Mammy, do you think I am fat?"

"You're a big girl – you get that from Dad – you could do with slimming down a bit."

"So you think I am fat."

"Not fat, just heavy."

"Fat."

"For Christ's sake, Jennifer, leave me alone! You asked for help – I sent you to the doctor – what more do you want?"

22

"I can't ever be like the others! They're tiny and I am a big fat horse! So there you go – I am fat – just say it – I know you think it!"

"Please just leave me alone – think what you want – you asked for help – what more can I do?"

My mother was of the generation not to question the doctor and I began to take the tablet every day, as prescribed. None of my sisters questioned the tablets – in fact I think they had no idea I was taking them at first. It would be four years and a change of doctor before we received the information that it was an amphetamine I was taking – otherwise known as speed. I then had to be slowly withdrawn from it to avoid going cold turkey.

Once I had been on the tablets about a month I became over-energetic, had trouble sleeping and felt happy all the time. This lasted a few months, then I began to hate myself even more. I used to phone the Samaritans from the phone box across the road from our house. I cried and told whoever was listening how much I wanted to die

"Surely life can't be that bad? You're a young girl with your whole life ahead of you. What makes you want to kill yourself?"

"No one wants me. My family don't notice me and, as for my mother, she buys me stuff but I just want her to make the pain go away!"

I would talk to them until my money ran out. I was telling strangers what I should have been telling my family. I was so sure that they didn't care about me, it would take a miracle before I would tell them anything. It did help to talk to these strangers on the phone but every night before bedtime I had a dose of my new 'medicine'. I have no idea why but somehow I would take

23

an almost masochistic pleasure from my burning throat.

The fact that I believed my mother supported the slimming pills left me feeling cold. Everyone knew I was fat but none of them had the guts to say it. I don't know what was going through my mind or how it worked during this time. All I know is that I had very low self-esteem and hated living. I truly believed that I was unlovable.

I was kept back in sixth class. The Head did not feel I was ready for secondary school. I was now tagged as stupid. My friends left Scoil Ide and went on without me. I had to start over, try and make new friends with the girls in an already established class. They had all known each other since junior infants; I had no chance with them. I was an outsider invading their space. I was also just beginning to take my slimming pills at that time. It seemed that everything happened around the same time – the eating disorder, slimming pills and being kept back in school. How much can a young girl handle? I would lie awake for hours at night; I had so much energy from the pills and too much time to think.

Girls are bitches and I was a target of the remarks of my classmates at times. They found the idea of me being kept back a source of conversation. I must be thick – after all, I was the only one kept back! I was either thick or a troublemaker; they had difficulty deciding which one. I became the class clown in an attempt to fit in, often disrupting lessons and being sent to the office for a slap on the hands. This somehow endeared me to the girls and they began to include me in their gangs. I was Jennifer the funny one; you could always rely on me for a laugh.

Thankfully two new girls came to the school, Anita

and Suzanne, and we stuck together, the new girls. I liked them both and enjoyed their company. I never told them about my secret though; it was the one thing that kept me strong.

My mother was very generous with me and I used to buy sweets for everyone with my money. Anything to be accepted.

I began to act out my feelings in anger and during my early teens I was not a very nice person. I had fantasies of killing my sisters. I hated them and their slim bodies. I wanted them to disappear so I didn't have to see them.

I had very large breasts so young and, in my attempts to hide them under baggy jumpers, I looked fat. My brother John took great pleasure in calling me a beached whale. He found himself so funny that at times it was difficult for him to get words out as he tried to hold back the laughter. We would all be sitting around the table as Mam put dinner up. Then he would start – and of course everyone in the room joined in. I felt the whole world was laughing at me – what did I do to be like this?

The rivalry between John and me was intense. Neither of us had a kind word to say about the other. Some of my friends fancied him. I would tell them they were insane to try, and put them off. How could the people I palled with fancy my creep of a brother? It was just wrong! I know that my words made little difference and my friends still thought John was great. In return for my attempts to turn the girls off him, he bestowed upon me the nickname 'Gibbon'. This was to follow me for years and caused deep pain every time I heard it. Everyone thought it was very funny – even my mother called me 'Gibbon' a few times. The fact that I was being likened to an ape further intensified my feelings of self-hatred. I was not fit to be human!

John went off to join the Navy at sixteen and I felt a great sense of relief – I would no longer have to deal with his jibes.

Eating disorders are secret and keeping that secret empowers you so much that it gives you the strength to keep going. I would protect myself from the mockery with the knowledge of what I was going to do later. It was weird but I used to purge as if I was doing it *to* my brothers and sisters. It was like each heave was inflicted on them. Most important of all, eating disorders are a manifestation of deeper emotional problems. Although I had a feeling I was not well, I managed to push it away. I was only doing this to myself because it was the only way I could expel the pain and hurt I felt inside. I was not mad, I was hurting, and this was my cry for help. I wanted to be caught as much as I wanted to keep the secret. Purging my pain away could gain nothing. I just didn't know it.

With early teens came an interest in boys. I was always interested in First Aid and when I was thirteen joined the Order of Malta, a voluntary service providing First Aid for football matches etc. It was also a good source of boys. During an Order of Malta disco a few weeks after I joined, a gorgeous boy asked me to dance. We danced for two hours – and he asked me to go out with him! Mike O'Reilly was a kind gentle human being, and when we had our first fumbled kiss all I could see was his smiling face. For two weeks I was walking on air and had no bad thoughts

– only romantic visions of Mike and myself, the wedding, babies and our house. The flush of first love, so perfect. I actually felt worthy. Then a new girl joined the Order of Malta and she was beautiful, so beautiful that the demons returned. I broke up with Mike. Believing that he would dump me for this girl, to avoid the humiliation I got in first and broke my own heart. He never did ask her out. Four years later Mike died tragically and I have visited his grave ever since as Mike was the first person to treat me like I was normal – no jibes, just holding hands, and coy smiles every now and then as we tried to wrap a dummy in bandages at the Order of Malta meetings.

After breaking up with Mike my bulimia escalated. At the same time I was getting ready for secondary school. I was to be the oldest in the class and this bothered me. I began a cycle of intense bingeing. I would sit in my bed at night listening to Cat Stevens while gorging on crisps and chocolate. I would crush the crisps and crumble in a few Chocolate Flakes, then eat the lot with a spoon, all the while with tears running down my face. I could eat a six-pack of crisps and four Flakes on a single binge, followed by toast and jam. I would then purge the lot down the toilet.

I went on like this for a few years. My weight remained normal enough as I would often go a few weeks without acting on my bulimia. I was still on the slimming tablets, which helped a bit; it made it easier for me to binge as I believed I would not gain any weight as long as I took the pills and purged. I had dreadful mood swings as a result of the Iomen – I would feel anger building up inside me and wanting to explode. I buried the feelings away. I remember watching *The Hulk* one day on the TV and daydreaming about having the power to explode like him. If only!

Secondary school was wonderful and I was enjoying myself. I had a large circle of friends and laughed more than I cried for a couple of years. But as always the demons came back to haunt me. This time I just binged. I am not sure what set the cycle off and my memory is blank as to what the cause might have been but I know something happened. I probably fancied someone and was rebuffed. When you hate yourself as much as I did the simplest things can set off a cycle of abuse. The weight piled on and I became the monster I feared most. At sixteen I was fourteen stone.

I never had a boyfriend after Mike O'Reilly and allowed the lads to use me for a quick feel, only ever letting them kiss me or touch my breasts. All my friends had boyfriends and I had one-night stands – after all, that's all I was good for.

During this time, I binged but couldn't purge, and this deepened my feelings of worthlessness. Every time I tried to purge I just cried. I don't know why this happened; it just did. I found comfort in junk food and after I would cry in pain for eating; yet I didn't purge! I know now that bulimia can run in cycles or on one action alone: either bingeing or purging. I was now in what is known as the binge cycle. I was gorging on food and could no longer expel it. This was a pretty horrendous time for me. I longed for physical comfort such as hugs and kisses – with none available I found solace in food.

I learned in recent years that some of the girls in my class were afraid of me! Did I come across as a bully? I don't know. I do know I was terrible for laughing at the swots. It was jealousy, if anything; I was often bemused as to how some people could be so clever! Always getting the A or on a bad day a B in their homework. 'If you can't join them, laugh at them' was my motto. I guess it was a case of the bullied becoming the bully.

I would often see the bully around the place. He would always say, "Hi, any news?" or something along those lines. I was very confused by this – had he no idea what he had done to me?

In second year we started getting free milk. Realising that the smell of sour milk is sickening, a couple of us would spill a bit behind a radiator in the classroom. Just a drop would stink the place – it was a blast!

We had this nutcase of a music teacher. She was totally off her head and would have us all reciting 'ta ta toffeti ta' to music notes on the board! I have never understood how this rhyme of hers would help us play the recorder better! I swear the woman was nuts! She would change mood at the slightest thing, one minute happy, the next red-faced and angry. She had white hair and very white skin to match. When she got angry her face became so red she looked like an escapee from the asylum. We were highly amused. I took a condom full of water into one of our music exams, and we passed it around continuously and whoever received it had to say "Ta". Laughter got the better of us and we were caught. It was so funny we all almost wet ourselves. We were so easily entertained that it made the resulting slap worth it. She just disappeared one day and we decided she had been caught – I can remember telling some innocent First Years that the asylum had recaptured her during our class.

I had decreed my fate by being the clown and at times

trying to think up things to do was hard work. Some of the teachers hated me and I played on this. I would target their class. I would stand up and ask some ridiculous question totally unrelated to the subject we were discussing. I can remember asking in maths class why Africans were black? When the teacher became angry I just said: "Well, you teach Civics too so I thought you might know. It's been really on my mind." Her hands were tied – what could she do? Punish me for appearing interested? It was just a case of "Sit down and be quiet!" and she knew I knew this. I asked geography teachers why the sky was blue and French teachers how to say six in Spanish. I have a feeling that all the teachers at my Graduation Mass were praying that I didn't repeat.

We changed doctors when I was about sixteen. I think the eccentric old guy had retired or something. I went to see the new GP and to her horror she discovered I was taking the Iomen! Immediately she began to take me off them. My mother was shocked to learn what they were. Having never asked, she presumed that they were harmless – in fact she too had taken them for a short while. The new doctor, realising that I was very overweight, planned a diet for me. She had no idea I was bulimic and this just pushed me further into despair.

I still had a large group of friends but I believed that they all hated me. I was only wanted in the gang to make them look good. After all, a fatty like me showed off their slim figures all the more. They had no idea of my feelings and I played along with the friendships. I really liked the girls: Anita, Suzanne, Helena, Helen, Noreen and Marina.

We named ourselves the BBB's: Big Bust Beauties! Our friendship was fun and enjoyable but always I held back a bit as I still believed I was being used. We had the usual gang of lads which girls tend to hang about with in their teens. The lads also had an overweight friend and we were constantly slagged about being in love! The two fat people were paired off while the normal people dated each other. I never dated this guy but as a friend I had great affection for him – in many ways I believed we were suffering a similar fate. I bet if people knew my secret, they would probably have decided that this guy and I binged and purged together – sure, don't all fat people do the same things?

We used to go to the Oasis nightclub as a gang and it was there I discovered cannabis and smoked it every Thursday and Friday night if I could afford it. Then I was free from my problems and calm as a still ocean.

On one particular Friday night a couple of years later, I lost my virginity on the sofa in my sister Dolores' hair salon.

I had a key as I washed heads for her, to earn money for my nights out. I would do cheap haircuts and colours for my friends at night, then one evening I managed to dye one of the lad's hair green! All he wanted was highlights. That was the end of my extra few quid! I was no longer trusted to do my friends' hair. Can you blame them? I only told Lolo about it years later.

So that Friday I went back with one of the lads and, with no passion or emotion, we had sex. Neither of us fancied the other and just had shag for the sake of it. High on cannabis, everything makes sense. The guy didn't even believe it when I told him I was a virgin! I had a bit of a reputation for one-night shifting. I gather one of them had exaggerated our encounter but, you know what, I didn't care what people thought of me. I was nothing, had no purpose on this earth. I just went home and binged some more.

My relationship with my family was still a strange one. I was very close to Honor and at times to Gabrielle, yet never discussed my problems with either of them. Looking back, I wonder why. Maybe I was so used to abusing myself by this time, I was afraid of help!

Honor was always constant in my life. Andy told me once when he was making fun of me that she was my mother! They also told me I was adopted. I don't know why they all enjoyed telling me I didn't belong. It was a great laugh.

Gabrielle would be nice to me for a week, then drop me as soon as something better came along. It hurt and still does today.

As for the others, I had no idea how to behave with them. John was off travelling with the Navy, Brian passed through the house on Sundays – and as for Andy, I have still to work him out! I had a soft spot for him and I knew if I went to him with my problems he would have helped. The only thing that put me off was that I would be forever indebted in return.

Dolores was dating a millionaire who drove sports cars. We were all a bit fascinated by him. Dolores was loud and in your face – she would often make fun of me in front of people, for no reason other than entertainment. Her fun was my pain.

Mary was married and had her family – I never really spent time with her or got to know her as she married and left home when I was very young. Sandra was always there and sometimes would come out with my friends and me. But I knew I couldn't talk to her about my problems. We just weren't close enough.

And as for my mother and father, we had the odd chat here and there. They were getting old. Dad had retired from work when I was fourteen and they tried to settle back into a quiet life. I don't think Mam would have understood if I did tell her – after all, bulimia was unheard of!

I sometimes wonder if deep down I knew I was special and loved by my parents but just couldn't face it. If I accepted their love then I would have to accept my problems. It was easier to believe they didn't care. I was messed up in so many ways but I knew that as long as I hated myself so much, I could never accept anyone's love, not even my parents. This was made easier for me by the fact that Mam was not very tactile – in fact she had not been since her mystery illness when I was a child. Dad was never one for hugs and kisses, so I had no worries there. If my parents had held me I am sure I would have broken down on the spot. The past would have been revealed and, who knows, maybe even healed.

I was always out or in my room bingeing. I avoided contact with my family as much as possible. Typical teenage behaviour, and the depressions and highs were always accredited to my age. My subliminal attempt to send out the message that something was wrong with me was met with "She must be in love" or "The girls must have had a falling out". I would sit and look at my food, then just push it around the plate, or say to my sisters how fat and ugly I felt – they just never got it. What I was trying to say was: "Help me, please!" They probably wouldn't have known how, even if they knew how much I hurt.

Andy's and Dolores' stories telling me I was adopted really bothered me. I did not look like the family and I used to wonder if they were telling the truth. I had built up a fantasy family in my mind who understood my innermost feelings and did everything they could to help me. I had a mam and dad and one sister who devoted all her time to talking to me about my feelings. I used to lie on my bed and go into my secret world. It helped a bit but I needed the real world to understand me.

I often wonder, if I had spoken out, what would have happened? Would I have been laughed at or helped? I can just see the whole family in the sitting room on a Sunday morning as I stand up and say:

"I detest myself and used to vomit for four years and took slimming pills. Now all I do is binge and hope I have a heart attack and die. Oh, and by the way, I believe you all hate me too."

I can just hear my mother: "Stop that kind of talk! Of course we all love you. Now stop all the nonsense and sit down!"

Eating disorders were unheard of so I can hardly blame people for not understanding my despair. I just wish they knew that all the jokes and laughter at my expense were like knives in the heart for me. I may have made light of it all at the time but the hurt ran deep. I desperately wanted my family to know my pain and help me.

I would have loved hugs and kisses with constant reassurance that I was loved. I wanted to hear them all say: "We had no idea you felt this way and are so sorry for not helping you!"

That never came and even today no one understands what I was going through – in fact there is an air of disbelief around the subject. My sisters are convinced that they would have known about my bulimia if it were happening! They need to think back and ask themselves how much of their time was spent with me during my dark days! I came out about my bulimia eleven years ago and I have yet to have an in-depth conversation about it with any of my family. When I do try, I get the 'we would have known' quote, so I give up!

Dolores is beginning to understand bit by bit. Her mind is open now and she listens more – still, it took a traumatic experience in her own life for her to see the world differently. I most certainly would not be telling you she is beginning to understand me had she not survived breast cancer last year. It brought us closer and we have respect for each other now, something that was missing before.

I never stopped wanting to die, but the angel on my shoulder held me back. I had access to pills – and often held them in my hand – wanting to swallow the lot. My weekend joint, when I could afford it, helped me forget my problems.

3

Leaving school and having to decide a future was a very distressing time for me. I hit the scales at sixteen stone by this time. The one thing I knew for sure is that I had to get away. To where and to do what? I had no idea. I just knew I had to leave. I could no longer exist in Galway; I had to start again. Galway was now the city of despair for me; I could find no comfort there. I had to leave; maybe then my life would be better. I had worked for Dolores for a couple of years and when I left school I just fell into the job of hairdressing, something I had never wanted to do.

I would stand in the sitting room at times looking at the photograph of my second birthday. I can remember how Mam used to put that one big curl in the front of my hair, and then kiss me. She called it my kiss curl. What I would have given to go back and start again! I would stare at the photo and wish I could go and exist in it. That little girl, so cute and perfect, was now the monster that was me!

My friend Anita and I went to Spain in the summer of '86. In the weeks leading up to our holiday I began to purge again and take laxatives in an attempt to reduce my size for the beach. With only three weeks' notice it was impossible to do but by God I tried!

Anita fell in love in Spain and I was left alone. Having time on my hands to think, all the old feelings and pain descended on me. With a constant supply of beautiful bodies around the pool, the despair clouded over me once more. I decided when I returned from Spain I would definitely leave Ireland and start again. I made this decision while kneeling on the bathroom floor, sunburned and puking up my lunch from earlier.

Leaving was never going to be easy. My mother wanted all her children around her. The only person to leave before me was John. Even though she was very proud of him being in the Navy, I know if he had come home my mother's heart would be filled with joy – all her children back in the nest!

I have no idea why my relationship with Mammy was so strained but I feel my self-loathing played a part. I was angry with her for not seeing what was before her eyes. A damaged young woman needing love. Deep down I knew she loved me, but not in the way I needed her to. I came into the family at a time when she was worn out, rearing children. 'The shakings of the bag' I was known as. One child too many; and when I needed help, her time was consumed with other things. I even joined the choir with her in the hope of a better relationship. I thought if we had similar interests then everything would be OK.

I know that her life had been hard and filled with stress, worrying about the nine of us. After that Black Day when she forgot who I was and was put on Valium, she seemed to change and had difficulty expressing herself. I wanted to be told I was wonderful and praised for any achievements along the way. No matter what I did, it never seemed to stir any great emotion. So what was the point in staying? Now all I had to do was plan my departure.

To avoid conflict, I decided that I would go for six weeks first. Most of my friends had moved to London by this time and it made sense for me to go too. I went to stay with Helen and Helena, a couple of friends from my schooldays, in their flat in Fern Barnett. As I had little money I looked for a job, pretending at interviews I was staying permanently. I got a job in a dry cleaner's that paid weekly.

I had a ball and during the six weeks my eating problems were suppressed. We talked, laughed and had a good time, but I never let on how I was feeling inside – my problems – my pain. I really felt alive. I had not laughed so much since my schooldays. I felt comfortable in their company, and still the words would not come out.

A couple of days before I went back to Ireland, Helena, her sister Martina and I went out to eat. We ended up in a restaurant in Victoria called Biguns Ribs. It was a real comfort food stop. We ate, drank and enjoyed ourselves.

A couple of the waiters were making eyes at us and they invited us to a nightclub after their shift. Mehmet and Anton were Turkish and in London to study English. They seemed like good fun guys, so off we went. As the night went on, I ended up shifting Mehmet. He was quite a looker but almost ten years older than me and I remember thinking: "What is this guy doing kissing a sixteen-stone lump of lard?" Anton took Martina out on the floor and at the end of the evening we all walked to Trafalgar Square for the night bus.

Mehmet gave me his phone number and begged me to call him. I promised and had a final kiss before boarding the bus. Helena, who was always the sensible one, told me to dump the phone number. I can clearly remember her saying: "He's paranoid – I would stay away if I were you!"

Words that would haunt me for years. Martina put Anton's number in the bin but I, like a fool, held on to Mehmet's.

Arriving back in Ireland, I made it clear to all I would be leaving again as soon as I had the money. No one believed me and just went along with it all. Within days of returning home to Galway I was bingeing again and a few weeks later I began to purge. It went in cycles.

For some stupid reason I phoned Mehmet one night, all the while with Helena's words ringing in my ears. A phone call was harmless, wasn't it? Surely nothing bad could happen just by passing time chatting to him?

So began a long-distance romance with letters and phone calls for the six months it took for me to leave. I was twenty-one and still had not been in any kind of relationship since Mike O'Reilly.

Mehmet started to say he was falling in love with me and I believed him – I was happily falling in love with the very idea that someone loved me.

He came to Ireland for a week, shortly before I left to stay in London. Gabrielle let him stay in her flat and my parents were going nuts. They took an instant dislike to him. My mother said he was sly and my father found him to be ignorant. I spent as much time as possible with him, showing him around Galway. We never slept together while he was in Ireland – it was just kissing and the odd fumble.

Mehmet mentioned my weight during his stay and I told him I was dieting. He was delighted to hear this as he said I was too fat to be his girlfriend. The subject never came up again during his stay.

Virgin Airways had begun to fly out of Dublin in the August of '87 and tickets for the first two flights were only £15! I had nothing saved but bought a ticket for the second flight out anyway. On the 3rd of August 1987, I walked out of my home against my parents' wishes with only £20 in my pocket. I remember Mammy and Daddy sitting in the kitchen warning me if I went out that door I was never to come back!

I picked up my bag and out I went. I believed that I had a man who loved me waiting on the other side. He had promised to be there at the airport and I had butterflies as I thought of meeting him again.

4

I made my way to Dublin airport, unconcerned about my parents' warning. Didn't all parents make such threats under pressure? They had hoped I would work with Dolores in the salon – not a hope in hell. I hated hairdressing. I only did it for the money to go out.

After the usual check-in I was more concerned with finding my gate and, after what seemed like an eternity waiting there, finally boarded the plane. My nerves got to me – but after a moment of uncertainty I sat back as my plane roared down the runway.

I dreamt of the fairytale to come.

My bag seemed to take forever to come up the baggage belt. I was close to getting on the belt to look for it when it finally appeared. I loaded my trolley and checked the hair and make-up before making my way through the Arrivals door where Mehmet would be waiting.

Scanning the crowd with a smile almost breaking my jaw, I searched the sea of faces for him over and over again until I had to accept he was not there. Maybe he got the time wrong or the Tube broke down? I went over every possibility I could think of for his no-show, then took a seat and patiently waited for my love to appear. I imagined how we would laugh over the reason for his delay. Not for a single moment did I believe he would not turn up.

After waiting three hours I telephoned the restaurant where he worked and they confirmed he was off for the day. What could have happened? I had spoken to him only last night to confirm the time I would arrive and he had promised to meet me, yet there was no sign of him. Why?

I waited another hour before getting the Tube to Brixton and a taxi to his flat. I knew the address but had never been in the place.

As my taxi rounded the corner to the block of flats I saw Mehmet come out of the stairwell. Shouting at the driver to stop, I jumped from the cab and ran to him, begging the answer to the question "Why were you not at the airport?"

Mehmet told me to pay the cab and come up to the flat – that he wanted to talk to me. I did as I was told – the flat was a dirty dark place with a mattress on the floor of every room. We sat at the kitchen table with a cup of black tea – there was no milk so I had no choice but to stomach the unfamiliar taste. Mehmet went on to explain in an unemotional tone how I was too fat to be his girlfriend. He had never thought that I would actually come to London to be with him.

"I can't be with you, Jennifer. You're fat and I don't like fat women."

"So why the hell did you say you loved me and wanted to be with me, for the past few months? You said only last night, when I told you my flight details, that you loved me! Why do this to me? Why?"

"Look, you are too bloody fat and it was all a joke! I can't be with a woman like you. Anyway, I have a girlfriend – she is from France and we are living together. I was going to meet her off the bus when you turned up."

In she walked: blonde, thin and beautiful. I had nothing to offer a man who had such a beautiful girlfriend.

"Hi, Monique, this is my friend Jennifer from Ireland – you know, the girl I told you about who is having trouble with her family?"

"Oh, hello, nice to meet you," she said with an outstretched hand which I had no option but to take in mine.

Monique had soft sallow skin and perfect nails.

Mehmet had told her about me all right but lies, all of it was lies. This woman thought I was running away from my family! Nice to see Mehmet had the cover story in place 'just in case'.

"Hi," I managed to squeeze out from my swollen throat as the tears welled up.

She sat on his knee so naturally I could see this was no new relationship – he had been with this woman a very long time.

I had to think and quickly. I had no money and nowhere to stay. I was in London, alone and broken-hearted.

"I have a bit of a problem, Monique – could I stay the night and get a room in the hostel tomorrow? My flight was late and they don't take people in after six so the only place I could come was here."

"Sure, no problem, the sitting room is empty. Why not

bed down there for the night? I don't mind at all – what about you, Mehmet?"

"Yeah, that's fine with me."

I spoke no more to Mehmet that night. Monique went to their room to watch TV and study. He followed. I lay awake all night and sometime around midnight I heard them make love! I was sure that it was for my benefit. I bet he normally didn't grunt so loudly every time.

There were about six people living in the flat, all on mattresses. I could hear them come in and go to the kitchen. I kept the room door closed and prayed that God would help me survive this mess, while my parents' words rang in my ears. I decided not to give in and go running home. I would find a way to get by. My friends had all lived in St Louise's hostel at one time or another. I would go there in the morning. I devised a story to tell the nuns – I knew from the girls that normally you had to book a room there. I needed to be in a state of urgency to get a bed – I would tell them I was sharing a flat with a friend who had suddenly moved in with her boyfriend, and that I could not afford the flat alone.

At seven the next morning I washed my face and brushed my teeth, then took my bag and made my way alone with the six pounds I had left in my pocket. I caught a bus, a Tube, then another bus. I had exactly three pounds twenty-five left for my new life by the time I reached the door of the hostel. Thankfully the nuns bought my story and offered me a bed. The tears that I cried were very real and I guess they could tell that I was distraught – if they only knew why! I explained my lack of cash and was given a letter for the Welfare who in turn gave me fifty pounds emergency money. I then went off and registered with the temp agency up the road. By the end of my first full day in London, I had a bed, some money and the possibility of work. What I didn't have was my dignity or soul!

Mehmet had played me. I was a fool – nothing but a fat ugly fool. I had not eaten for two days but the pain in my heart was so bad I had to purge in the hope of getting some relief. My life was over and I had no need to live. I decided to starve myself to death!

"Mehmet wants thin – I'll give him thin!"

I went about my new life in a daze, doing a bit of temping here and there, then out of the blue one day the Reception called up to say I had a visitor! I had been living in the hostel for a month by this time and had minimal contact with home. Two of my mother's sisters lived in London and I had been waiting for her to send one of them to see if I was OK. I knew Mammy couldn't survive without someone telling her where and how I was living. So, expecting it was one of my aunts checking up on me, I went down with a pre-prepared speech. I had my answers ticked off: "Yes, I am eating well – of course I don't go out late – no, I have nothing more to do with him."

As I entered Reception I nearly had a heart attack.

There in front of me stood Mehmet.

"What do you want?" I asked.

"I just wanted to make sure you were OK."

"Why? So you could insult me some more?"

"No, I was worried about you."

"Of course you were – you must be running low on entertainment so you came looking for me. What do you want?"

"To give you this."

Mehmet handed me a bag full of cans, the name Herbal Life stamped all over them.

"What's this? You think vitamins will solve everything! Take away the hurt you caused me? How dare you come here – offering me a bag of herb drinks and vitamins, thinking everything will be OK! Guilt is an awful thing to live with, you know!"

"Look, just shut up and listen, will you? This woman came into the restaurant and she was telling me how she lost six stone on this stuff. I bought it for you so that you can get thin and then maybe we can be together. I can't be with you while you're fat – people will laugh at me."

"What about Monique? I thought you two were very happy together?"

"Never mind her! I am offering you a chance to be with me – it's up to you – take it or leave it. I will come and see you every week and then we will see how it's going."

Desperate for a chance of love, I would have done anything, so I took the cans and said goodbye without any idea of what had just happened between us! Later my sick brain told me that he did love me – otherwise why would he want to help me lose weight? I had the answer: lose weight and spend my life with Mehmet. I could feel the sensible part of my brain shouting, "He is a bloody fool – ignore him! If anyone needs pills and potions it's him! Preferably poisonous!"

I continued to do some temping, then one of the nuns who had taken a shine to me felt I needed guidance! She sent me over to the Irish Centre for an interview. I got the job and started the very next day. Everyone was so nice. I could forget my problems when I was at work.

Still, every evening the demons returned. I drank the shakes Mehmet had given me. My tears would flow and I would beg my body to be thin. Nobody at the hostel was aware of my problems. I would often get a Chinese with them in the evening and sit and chat like a normal person, then excuse myself and go and purge the lot in the loo.

I was at work one day and out of the blue my mother, Andy's wife Mary and John's girlfriend Helen arrived at the centre. I was shocked but delighted to see them.

"What are you lot doing here?"

My mother looked me in the eye and told me: "We are here to take you back home and away from that fella – he's no good and your place is at home."

I had told my mother during one of our strained phone calls that I was seeing Mehmet. I was still not forgiven for leaving home but I was beginning to think that we were getting along better, that Mam had accepted I had a new life in London.

I had no idea what the hell was going on. There must have been a family powwow and the troops were despatched to take me home! Not a chance in hell! I was living alone and wanted my own life but most of all I wanted to be thin so Mehmet would love me. No way were they taking me back! For me Galway signified despair – it was not a place I needed to be. But I hadn't a hope in hell of convincing my mother that I didn't want to go back with them! My refusal was seen as defiance. I kept thinking: you hate me anyway so why bother trying to mess things up for me now?

After a couple of days of them trying to get me to pack

up and go home, they gave up and left. I remember telling Mam I would be home for Christmas and she just looked at me! I had let her down. Choosing a Turkish man and a life in London over what she believed was the cosy family life she was offering me! If only I could have told her the truth! I hated living at home. I believed they all hated me and I was convinced that Mammy hated me too.

It was my secrets and lies that had damaged our relationship – keeping my secret was such an overpowering demand I had no choice but to stay in London. I needed someone to look after me. Mehmet was offering me this security.

I am not sure what the priest at the Irish Centre was told but I was let go! I have always had the feeling that my mother told him I was a runaway and he let me go in the hope I would go home to Galway. If I was right, the plan didn't work and I stayed. I drank my shakes and puked my food every day. After a few weeks Mehmet began to comment on the fact that I was losing the weight and I would smile, then go and punish myself for being so fat in the first place.

Bulimia is a difficult disease to understand but the feeling of bile in the throat and the pain it induces is a form of punishment for eating, and at the same time a comfort of sorts. I was now moving further down the line: my bulimia was becoming bulimia anorexia. After reading about Lady Diana I had a good idea of what my illness might be but, not wanting to face up to things, I preferred to believe that this was how my life was meant to be.

On one of Mehmet's weekly visits he asked me if I would

like to come and stay over at the flat that night. Believing that he had finally realised how foolish he had been, I agreed. I thought that I was being taken to what was to become my new home, that Mehmet wanted me to meet his friends before making our relationship official.

I walked in the door and saw Monique stand there.

"Hi, Jennifer! Have you come to say goodbye?"

I can't explain but there was something smart in her tone with me! She was going back to France in the morning and people had gathered to say goodbye. What was Mehmet playing at? Why bring me to say goodbye to his lover and did she know something? I was so confused I wished I could run.

I stayed and was introduced to the flat's occupants, three other Turkish men. They seemed nice and friendly. I managed to speak to the youngest guy, Mo, through broken English. I was in a surreal world that night and it was to be a long time before I understood why I was there.

I stayed the night and the following morning everyone gathered to say goodbye to Monique. I shook her hand and she bent to my ear and whispered, "He is all yours now!"

I was startled by what she said but deep down I knew that I was going to be her replacement as much as she did. Monique was going back to France to finish her law degree and had no further use for Mehmet. He carried her bags and took her to the airport like a dutiful partner. I didn't know what happened then – maybe they made promises to meet up again and be together? I was sure that this was not the end for them. I was convinced that Monique would forever be my nemesis. In fact, he never heard from her again.

I headed back to the hostel to get ready for work, still very confused by what had happened in the previous twenty-four hours. What kind of man takes a woman he says he loves to say goodbye to his lover! I worked on autopilot that day.

After work I was walking back to St Louise's when I saw Mehmet leaning against the railings.

"What are you doing here?"

"I just want to talk to you about our future."

"What future? I was unaware we had one."

"Look, Monique is gone. You know what you have to do to be with me. You're not as fat as you were and we still have a way to go but I will let you move in as long as you promise to get rid of the ugly fat. I told you before, I don't want a fat woman."

My head was in a state of confusion. The correct response would be to tell him to get lost. Who the hell did he think he was? He was attractive but not a bloody Adonis and any woman with a bit of sense would laugh in his face.

But I was not normal and welcomed the tiniest morsel of affection and even though I knew this man was a user I was willing to accept him into my life.

"Look, I'm tired and need to have a shower and a good sleep. I'll discuss this with you tomorrow."

"Remember, this is your only chance. If you can't decide by tomorrow there is a Spanish girl at college who wants me."

I wanted to tell him he was a wanker but all I said was that we would talk tomorrow. Then I went in and made myself purge to heal the pain. I had only consumed an apple and cups of tea since the day before and had to force the purge more than normally as my stomach was empty. I went to bed with a burning throat from the bile but the pain kept my mind off the real reason for my distress. I was not ready to face the reality of what I was about to do: freely give myself to a man who wanted only to use and hurt me! I knew it was so very wrong but I could not resist. I had nothing to fight for any more. I was a worthless human being, wasting the planet's oxygen by my very existence. At that point I wished I was dead but I was too weak to even fulfil that desire. As I began to fall asleep I was sure I heard a gentle voice whisper: "You are a good person and I love you." Believing in angels, I was comforted by the thought that mine was with me that night.

5

I moved in with Mehmet the following evening. I told the nuns that I was going to try living with a friend. I wanted to keep my options open and would continue to pay rent to the hostel until I was sure.

Mehmet left me to move alone, just giving me Monique's old key – it even had a key ring with her name on it!

This was an insensitive uncaring man, who left me standing on the street telling me he would be home later.

"Move your stuff into my room – that is where you will be staying and I will speak to you when I get home."

His room consisted of a mattress on the floor with a washed-out blue duvet set, a chair and a TV in the corner. The floor was bare and you had to be careful of the nails sticking out of the floorboards. So this was going to be my home. I felt a shiver go down my spine at that point. All my natural instincts were crying out to me: "Don't do it, Jennifer, it's a mistake! Run!" Ignoring my inner voice I began to unpack my clothes, wondering what was the point? There was no wardrobe to put them in. I began to make neat piles on the floor. I found a box downstairs which I turned over and put my make-up and toiletries on – a makeshift table that was to hold my stuff for the next few years.

Mehmet came home at about two in the morning smelling of booze. I had been sitting staring blankly at the TV all night. I had no idea what I had watched. I just knew it was on. He came into the room without any acknowledgement of my presence, undressed in silence, then sat on the edge of the mattress and began listing the rules I had to abide by.

"If you really want to be with me you have to get rid of the disgusting fat on your body. If it's not gone very soon then you will have to go. I keep telling you I can't be with a fat woman and until you are thin I will not take you out with me. I don't want my friends to see you."

"What am I? Some kind of awful secret you want to keep locked in the room?"

"Look, how many times do I have to explain myself?" he said angrily. "When you're thin we can be together. Until then, we are just friends to everyone else outside this house."

"I am not sure about this, Mehmet. Do you hate me so much that I must be hidden away or are you looking for a woman to use? What am I?"

"For fuck sake, you stupid woman, if you get thin we will be a couple!" he said furiously. "If not, it's out the door! You either want me or not. Make your stupid mind up!"

His anger made me fearful. I was trapped. I had no love for myself so how could I expect others to care? The solution seems to be to get thin. Then my life would be fine. Mehmet would love me and proudly show me off to his friends. I would then have the courage to love myself. For now I had to be hidden away.

"OK, Mehmet, we will try it and see how everything works out. You know I want to be with you. If this means I must sacrifice socialising with you for now, then that's how it has to be."

He turned and kissed me. It was not the soft romantic kiss I had expected! It was wet and forceful. I had not been with Mehmet before. I had imagined our first time would be soft and romantic. I had created a fairytale in my head – even now I was adding to the story – how this beautiful woman suddenly appears from the dark dingy room where she had been hiding just like a butterfly in her cocoon.

Mehmet did not make love to me that night – he had sex with me. No passion, no feeling and most of all no respect.

I got an evening job in a pizza restaurant near the flat and decided to study Hotel and Catering at college during the day.

Mehmet was not impressed with my new job and chastised me for eating pizza. "It's full of fat, you stupid cow! You will never lose weight eating pizza! Eat salad! If I catch you eating pizza again you're out, you hear?"

Then he took the pizza I had brought home from work and ate it himself! Mehmet took all my wages from me. I would come home exhausted after a difficult shift and all he wanted was my tips! He was saving for our future, I was told. I should be delighted that he was taking such good care of me.

There was never any food in the house. Mehmet had all his meals at work and college. If I suggested going shopping he would react angrily

"You want to buy shit and fill your fat face. I only ever want to see low-fat food in this house!"

My bulimia was rampant by now – everything I ate I purged. My body was deprived of nutrition and it was no surprise when I began to get sick. I started to have kidney infections almost weekly and my GP referred me to a specialist. You could tell by the way he looked at me he knew there was something more than a kidney infection wrong with me. I have recently read the referral letter when I requested to see my medical notes. He wrote I was living with a Turkish man who wanted to take a thin wife home to his family in Turkey. I think my GP knew more than I had ever told him; maybe he had past experience? I don't know but he certainly had an insight into my life. At that time Mehmet and I had never even discussed marriage. It's unlikely I said anything to the doctor. He was Mehmet's GP also, of course, so maybe Mehmet had said something about my weight to him.

Before I received the appointment, I was rushed to the hospital one weekend from work with terrible pain. I was admitted and underwent tests, which indicated kidney stones although further tests were required before a definitive diagnosis could be made.

Christmas was close and I had a flight booked for the holidays. Mehmet was going to Turkey for Christmas and New Year and I was going home to Galway.

After a week in the hospital undergoing tests, I was

booked into St Thomas' Hospital for a 'procedure' in February.

Mehmet was completely unconcerned about my illness. He was more interested in what I would eat during the holidays. At the airport I was warned over and over – if I came back with weight on, I was not welcome. I was also told not to go out at night. I was to stay with my parents at all times. No pubs or clubs and especially no restaurants.

This was to be a difficult Christmas. I arrived at the door and my mother was hoovering her lush new burgundy carpet – she wanted me to see it at its best, she was so proud of it. Once I was over the threshold and the hugs and kisses were finished, she noticed how much weight I had lost. I had left Galway on the 3rd of August weighing sixteen stone and now, standing in the hallway the day before Christmas Eve, I was a little over ten. Everyone commented on how well I looked. They had no idea of the suffering I was enduring to look this way. My bulimia had escalated to the point where I was purging a single sweet, let alone a meal.

My parents knew I was with Mehmet – they didn't like it one bit – but for the sake of peace nothing was said. I talked about college and my job – I had nothing else to talk about – my 'prison cell' was never mentioned. I was almost caught by my mother one evening as I purged but got away with the dickey tummy excuse. I was so sorry that she had not actually caught me. Maybe then I could get help and be released from my prison. I cried tears of pain that night.

I portrayed happiness to those around me. Nobody

had the slightest hint of how unhappy I was. As usual everyone was consumed with their own life! My mother told me one evening about all the problems she was having. Jesus Christ, nearly everyone was married with children, so why was my mother still having problems? I told her she should let everyone fend for themselves! I was in my twenties and I was the youngest! No matter how old the rest of them were, Mammy still had to deal with their problems. My mother loved all her children equally and dedicated her life to us. I unfortunately was so filled with self-loathing I only recognised this when it was too late. I know that my mother forgives me for the way I behaved. I was sick and incapable of accepting love.

My sister Mary was drinking too much – it turned out eventually that she was alcoholic – and Mammy was worried about her. I remember thinking: "What about her husband? Can't he deal with it?" I felt so sorry for my mother – everything still landed on her doorstep!

I began to see my parents in a different light that Christmas; maybe it was because I stayed at home with them and talked. Here were two lovely people who had spent their lives providing for and protecting their family; and at a time when they both should have been retired, they still had to sort problems out. I guess I was just born at the wrong time to see them as they really were. I so much wanted to cry and hug them both but I couldn't. I knew if I did I would tell everything. I spent that Christmas holiday dying inside. I so loved my parents and they loved me yet I felt compelled to return to my cell against their wishes.

Mehmet had power and control over me. I don't know why I needed to be with him – I never loved him yet I was in a way addicted to him! I often wonder if I stayed to be punished. I felt I deserved nothing from life and Mehmet reinforced my feelings. I would lose sleep wondering what the attraction was but as soon as he spoke I obeyed. It was not fear but something much deeper.

I returned to London to the dark empty room that was my prison. Mehmet was not due back for a few days. One evening hunger plagued my body. So painful was my need to eat, I went to the shop and bought a tin of spaghetti and instant mash to fill me up and stem the pain. The secrecy of preparing such a pitiful meal was utter madness. I knew Mehmet was in Istanbul yet I went down the three flights of stairs with the empty tin and packet to conceal the fact that I had eaten. So intense was my fear of getting caught that I was afraid even with thousands of miles between us. I sat on the steps and cried. I begged for normality but it never came! Why was I living this life? I was in dire need of help but so totally incapable of asking for it.

Mehmet returned on the 5th of January and I was again in my cell. I went to college and work, then back to the room. Mehmet would only allow me to eat fruit and this was playing havoc with my digestive system. I used to sneak sometimes to McDonald's on my way home from college, just to feel the sensation of eating food. I would have been living on the fruit my jailor allowed me to eat for weeks on end when the urge to feel full would become so great I had to answer it. With my saved-up coppers I had a children's burger and chips!

Mehmet's friend Mo was deported in early February.

Immigration caught him working during a swoop of illegal workers. In Victoria Tube station the day after Mo was sent home, Mehmet informed me I had to marry him during the next couple of days or he too would be deported. I didn't really understand how the system worked but was happy to accept what he said.

He, of course, knew all the ins and outs. With an Irish wife, he eventually managed to acquire a British passport as a member of the European Union.

Of course, a long time after, with hindsight I realised he had probably planned the marriage from the start. He wanted a British passport and a naïve young Irish girl was an answer to prayer for him. Also, of course, the acquirement of an educated wife meant he could double his income. I never fully realised this at the time. Maybe deep inside I did have a notion of what was going on but I needed to believe he loved me for myself.

I married him two days later on the 6th of February in Brixton Registry Office and so, on my wedding night, began the cycle of physical abuse.

6

The day itself was a mess and not what any bride would want. Mehmet laughed as we took our vows and my ring cost five pounds from a cheap jeweller's in Brixton. I borrowed the clothes I wore which were way too big for me. No white dress or walking down the aisle, just a crowd of foreign nationals arriving at the Registry Office. When I saw the photos a friend had taken, I wondered what the registrar had thought of us? I was so embarrassed. Not how any bride should feel.

My sister Sandra and her husband Christy were at the wedding. They had moved to London to find work during Ireland's unemployment crisis. Sandra was my witness on my big day so at least I could say I had some family at my wedding. They weren't happy but at least they were there.

The wedding party, if you could call it that, went to a pub on Brixton Hill after a curry in our flat, which I cooked but was not allowed to eat. I stood and watched the guests eat as my stomach groaned with hunger.

It was in the pub I committed my crime. The barman was from Offaly and I spoke to him about life in London. Little did I know I would be beaten for it later. It seems the mental battering I was receiving did not satisfy Mehmet's desire to hurt me. For him, the marriage licence gave him the power to hit me when he felt like it or even just for entertainment.

The morning after my wedding I was bruised and sore but I had to try and make the effort – my sister Honor and her husband Ray were arriving in London later and I could not allow anyone to see what Mehmet had done to me. That day he had no aversion to make-up! Normally I was not allowed to wear the stuff – he said it made me look like a whore. I still had the make-up I brought from Ireland all those months ago. Today it was used to cover his actions and protect him.

Honor had no idea I had married Mehmet the day before. She was very shocked at what I had done. She was also very taken aback by the conditions I was living in. We had nothing but the mattress and TV and the rest of the flat was shared.

The main reason for Honor and Ray's visit was my upcoming hospital stay. I was going into St Thomas' Hospital the following day for the 'procedure'. I had never asked what it was exactly. But on admission I was told I was going to theatre for biopsies. I had been on long-term antibiotics and painkillers for almost three months – and nothing had improved. I had a feeling deep down that my bulimia might be a cause of the constant kidney infections but said nothing.

Honor had come because she was worried and wanted to be there for me. It was obvious that I had lost more weight since going home for Christmas. I was nine stone three when I was admitted to hospital on the Monday morning. Over a stone lighter in less than two months!

Honor kept asking me why there was no food in the house and would not accept we ate at work all the time as an answer. The remaining curry from the wedding had been thrown away just in case I was tempted to eat it. And the fridge was empty when she arrived. Mehmet had refused to allow me to buy anything, saying if they wanted to eat they could buy their own food.

"You look like death. What do you eat? There is nothing in the house, not so much as a biscuit!"

"We have all our meals at work. We are both working in restaurants and have no need to buy food. Just the basics."

"What about breakfast and the days you're not working? What do you eat then?"

She would not leave the subject alone and was also bothered by Mehmet's lack of concern for my health. When Honor wants answers, she gets them. By the time she went home she knew about the dieting and suspected the abuse. She witnessed how Mehmet ate all the sweets she had brought to the hospital for me! Very quickly she realised that Mehmet was starving me. He talked about how he hated fat women to her and how without his help I would never have lost the weight. She began to hide food in my hospital room. Packets of biscuits, crisps, drinks – hidden from Mehmet. I spent five days in the hospital and underwent a further battery of tests. My main 'procedure' was a kidney and liver biopsy. I would have to wait until my next appointment for the results.

I was so weak and brainwashed that Honor's cries to take me back home and leave this monster fell on deaf ears. I believed somewhere in my sick mind that I loved this man, that soon he would love me too. I felt hurt that Honor did not understand me. I knew once she went home the whole family would be aware of my circumstances and the calls to leave Mehmet and return to Galway would be unending.

Mehmet began to play on my feelings towards my family, constantly stating that none of them cared about me. Not a day went by when he did not criticise everyone. He, Mehmet, was the only person on earth with my best interests at heart. I believed him. After all, when that little girl, their sister and daughter, had needed support no one had been there for me.

I went back to the hospital for my results alone. The doctors were confused as I had scarring on both my liver and kidney! As for the cause of the scarring, they were at a loss. I knew deep down it was caused by my eating disorder but said nothing. I knew I was hurting myself and punishing my body through food. This was something so momentous that I knew I could not cope with the pain admitting I had a problem would bring.

For the next year I would be a regular at the clinic. Dr Jones would become more confused as time passed. All the treatment I received was unsuccessful; only I knew why. I was not going to tell them either.

Life at home was unchanged. The only food I consumed was fruit unless I had travelled to another London borough for a burger and chips. I used to save all my two-pence pieces until I had enough for a child's meal. It could take weeks to save the money but when the hunger became extreme I would travel by Tube and bus to Croydon or Hammersmith to satisfy my longing. The meal was never allowed time to digest. I would purge as soon as I returned home. It was the experience of eating I wanted and the need was met. No need to disrupt my diet by allowing the food into my system. Then I would start saving all over again for the next meal.

Mehmet was having difficulty at work and would often come home angry. I had begun to learn from his body language as to whether I was to pay for his unhappiness. The sound of the front door closing or the way he placed his cup on the table would alert me to an upcoming beating.

"You stupid bitch – you are ruining my life!" *Slap!* "You fat ugly whore!" I was pushed to the floor and he'd begin to kick me.

I remember thinking once it was lucky he removed his shoes when he came home – if he wore shoes in the room I would be dead. It was always the same: I was the reason for his mood! The words never changed: "fat ugly bitch", "stupid bitch", "fat whore". Mehmet's command of the English language was incomplete. Later he would learn how to better construct his insults.

I was Mehmet's punch-bag and there was no escape for me. When I knew he was about to start abusing me I would feel like a rabbit trapped in headlights, all my instincts telling me to run! Yet my body was unable to obey the command. I had nowhere to go. This man controlled my very existence. On my days off he would lock me in the flat. I would be left afraid and alone for up to twelve hours, more if he decided to go to a club with his friends. I handed over my wage packet every week and was given fifteen pounds to cover my travel card, milk and bread for the flat. I knew all the money went to Turkey. I was not stupid and knew he was building a house with my wages! No matter how well I behaved he had to beat me and take my wages. Sometimes I didn't know which hurt most, losing the money or the abuse.

At college I felt alive. Most of the other students were younger than me and I found their love of life infectious. I made friends with a girl called Maria who would plead with me to go out for a drink. I always used work as an excuse and eventually she stopped asking. Mehmet came to collect me from college one day and I introduced him to Maria. The next morning she began to ask questions about our relationship. She told me that she felt uneasy in Mehmet's company and I broke down and told her my story.

"Jennifer, you have to leave him! I know people who can protect you. Please let me help you!"

"I can't. I have no life. Mehmet controls everything – my money, food and when I can leave the flat."

"You don't need money to leave. Women's Aid can help you with a safe house and money."

"He will find me and then he will kill me. Maria, I am too weak to leave and too afraid to try. I know someday I will be free – this is what keeps me fighting, but right now I am not ready."

"Look, take this number – it's free-phone – and call them even if it's just to talk. My mother used to work on the helpline and I know that they will at least listen to you until you are ready to go. Promise me you will call them!"

"I promise and thank you for caring."

"You're my friend. Of course I care. You don't realise it but you are a lovely person and I believe without that bastard you can have a life filled with friends who will care about you. Trust me!"

I called the number from a phone box the very next day and spoke for over an hour to a guy called Paul. He kept reassuring me that they would always be there for me. If and when I was ready to leave Mehmet, they would provide all the support I needed. I asked him why I couldn't leave, what kept me there. He told me about 'Battered Women Syndrome' where women stay in abusive relationships for the fear of leaving. Once one has become used to a cycle, no matter how abusive, there is a safety in staying. The abuser makes a person feel useless and worthless without them. On average, a woman will leave an abusive partner up to seven times before she may be able to leave for good. Sadly many never leave. They told me to set up a secret 'run account', save even a pound a week and when eventually my time came, at least I would have some money to help with my new life. I not only had an eating disorder and kidney disorder but now I suffered from a syndrome! I was a total mess, not worth saving. I called Paul every week after that. I found that just by talking to him I was able to find an outlet for some of my pain. He never pushed me to try and leave Mehmet, believing that I would when the time was right for me.

7

When college broke up for the summer, Mehmet decided that I should go full-time in the pizza restaurant. He wanted to buy a holiday home in Turkey for us! I worked six days a week with the odd double shift thrown in and returned dutifully every night to my cell. Mehmet on the other hand lived life as a single man. His family was even unaware of our marriage. I would only find this out when his mother came to London for a holiday.

Mehmet decided before his mother came to visit that I was still far too fat for her to meet me. He decided that if I were to have cosmetic surgery to remove my now sagging tummy, then I would be acceptable. If I didn't have the surgery? Then I was to leave and get a divorce. Like a fool I handed over £2850, a loan I would have to pay off with my hard-earned money. I could not believe I was paying to allow a surgeon to cut me up. Two days before his precious mother arrived, I was admitted alone into a private clinic in Hammersmith for my operation. When the time came for me to go to theatre, I walked to the room like a person about to be executed. The nurses put it down to nerves. What I was really feeling was fear. The doctor was unaware of my eating disorder and my unresolved kidney problems. I was sure I was too weak for the surgery and that I would die.

I came round three hours later with a tight corset from my hips to my breasts and the most horrific pain. I stayed in overnight and was discharged early the following morning. Convinced I was far too unwell to be discharged, I stated this to the nurse who responded by telling me I had paid only for one night and would need to pay a further £250 to stay another night. Mehmet, who had turned up in the guise of the dutiful husband to take me home, refused to pay the money. I was a grown woman, he told me, and I was capable of looking after myself. Nothing about any help from him. Sure, I had been alone since I came into the clinic and the only reason he was here now was because he knew I would not be allowed to leave without being picked up. I was to be on my own again but this time I'd had my stomach cut off. The pain was unbearable. Just the thought of returning to my cell in this state made me weak. I was allowed to stay another hour to get my strength back. A cup of sweet tea and a biscuit that Mehmet ate, then I was sent on my way.

Going back to my cell was a nightmare journey. Mehmet left me in a taxi and went to meet friends at the Turkish café. He would sit and chat for the next five hours with his friends and then head off to work, while I had to get myself home. I was unable to stand straight and dreaded having to climb three flights of stairs unaided to get to my front door.

Once back in my room I found the fact the mattress was on the floor a huge obstacle. I could lie down but getting up required the help of another person. I was alone. I had to crawl to the door to use it to pull myself up by the handle.

Mehmet came home after midnight and did not so much as ask how I was. Every day this man showed a more sadistic nature and I grew ever more fearful. He had a nice comfortable life meeting his friends for Turkish coffee, eating in Turkish restaurants. I often wondered why he was in London when the only people he associated with were Turkish. But I would not dare ask. I obeyed and stayed in my cell while he enjoyed life to the full.

My mother-in-law Sebahat arrived the following day. At first I was startled: she was small and very rounded though all I could see were her eyes as she was covered with a veil and long coat. I had no knowledge of Islam – Mehmet had never discussed religion with me. It was obvious from his mother's appearance that the family were devout.

When we went inside Sebahat took her coat off – and I was looking in dismay at this very *fat* old lady. Why the hell did I have to be thin before we met? His mother was well overweight and I was angry as hell that I had to be cut up just to meet her.

She smiled a very sly smile and questioned her son. As she too was shocked to meet a woman unable to stand straight, she wanted to know why. Now he had to explain why I was in such a state. To cover up what he had forced me to do, he told her I'd had an operation on my kidney.

I only discovered his lies when I was alone with his

mother. She asked in simple Turkish what was wrong with my kidneys. I knew straight away the bastard had lied. Feeling ever more angry with him, I got out the dictionary and told her the truth – I also told her we were married! The shock on her face was clear to see. Her precious son had not only married outside his culture but his religion too! She probably had a young Turkish girl lined up for the shit.

I managed to get our mattress off the floor by collecting milk crates throughout the estate. The pain of getting up and down off the thing had reached unbearable levels. I begged Mehmet to buy a base but he refused so I did what I could: I used my initiative. I carried all twelve of them up three flights of stairs alone, just a week after my surgery. Mehmet offered no help – in fact when I was bringing in the last crate he laughed at me for my 'stupid idea that would never work'. Mehmet and Sebahat watched as I lay the crates side by side against the wall, only helping when I could not lift the mattress. My idea worked and I had a bed I could sit on and rest. No more crawling to the door to help myself stand up. I could raise myself up from the bed and stand.

My hovel began to look a bit better. I even had a bedside locker I bought in the second-hand shop for five pounds. How easily I was pleased!

A couple of weeks after the demon mother-in-law came to stay, my sister Sandra and her husband Christy moved into our flat to be nearer to work. They, unlike the previous tenants, would help with the bills. I am sure deep down Mehmet took pleasure in knowing he could torture me in front of my family. They were planning to spend another few months in London, make a bit of money and go back home. We had an empty room in the flat and it made sense for them to take it.

The hardest thing about having Sandra live with me was the food. They shopped every week and made a dinner every evening. The smell of food in the flat used to be hell for me. Christy would often invite me to eat with them but I always pretended I had eaten. They knew damn well I hadn't but I convinced myself they believed me. One night when Christy was making bacon and cabbage I gave into my desire and agreed to have dinner with them – but just before the food was served Mehmet came in and gone was my lovely dinner. If he saw me eat a full meal he would first chastise me and beat me later. Even with my sister and her husband in the flat he continued to beat me. I think he enjoyed it more, knowing there was nothing they could do. For some unknown reason they feared him and even if they decided to call the police during one of my beatings, Mehmet knew I would never give him up for fear of what he would do to me later.

I used to try and understand how he had the balls to hit me in front of people. I also could not understand how people were so fearful of this man they never intervened! If he had been told to stop just once, I might have gathered the strength to leave. I imagine I would have felt worth something if a person were to speak up for me.

My brother John and his girlfriend Helen had also witnessed the abuse. They stayed over with us on their way back from a holiday in Australia. Mehmet was not impressed and could hardly contain his delight when they moved on. On one occasion I was hit with a belt in full view. They tried the following day to get me to go home with them, but as usual I refused. I was sure my family also felt I was good-for-nothing, reinforcing my own feelings of self-hatred. As Mehmet said, I was nothing and no one wanted me – I was lucky he was trying to help me be a better person.

I remember talking to Sandra one night about how shocked I was that Sebahat was fat! She was fully aware of my lifestyle by now – I couldn't hide it when they were living with us. It's one thing hearing about a situation and another seeing it for yourself. I am not sure what they thought about it – it was never discussed really. I was asked a few times why I stayed and gave the usual 'I love him' answer.

In fact, at that time I couldn't care less what anyone thought. I was up to my neck in it with Sebahat and close to pulling my hair out. Mehmet left me to care for this old lady when I was unable to care for myself. I was not going to protect his reputation.

Having Sebahat to stay was hell on earth. She was a very demanding woman and refused to get herself so much as a cup of tea. It was my job to care for her! No one had told me this! I knew nothing about Turkish culture. Not only did I have to heal my oozing wounds, I was also expected to feed and entertain his mother. This woman had never been out of Turkey before, spoke no English and from what I could ascertain she was a walking bitch – I would be able to confirm this later. We communicated with the little Turkish I knew, but it was enough.

Mehmet had this pet name for me: *Siskoeim*. I had no idea of its true meaning, but when Sebahat used it a few times I was unnerved to say the least. Later, when I discovered its meaning, I would hate her all the more.

I used to think it meant something sweet until one day, during a conversation with a Turkish girl, I was informed it meant 'Fatty'. No wonder his Turkish friends laughed when he would cuddle me and call me 'Siskoeim' – 'My Fatty!'.

I had taken two weeks' holiday from work to have my surgery, believing the doctor's promise of recovery in such a short period of time. I ended up in the Casualty department. As I had not rested as instructed after my operation, I now had an infection in the wound! I remember thinking: "Not surprising really when you live on apples and bananas, have no aftercare and still have an unresolved kidney problem – oh, and your husband beats you." I wanted so much to tell the doctor everything, but as usual I chickened out! I went home with a collection of pills and had to take an extra week off work.

I eventually went back to work and my wound healed. The following week I had my corset removed for good. I had spent four weeks with this contraption holding my body together. Due to the infection my navel healed badly and part of it had fallen off! Disgusting was the only word I could think of! There was nothing I could do and I cried on the Tube all the way to work.

8

The mother-in-law stayed for six weeks. The only good thing about it was I had a sort of reprieve from the beatings in the sense that I was smacked across the face and pushed about but not given a full-on beating when she was there. He was saving this for later.

She was no sooner on Turkish soil but her wonderful son was at it again.

"You stupid bitch! My mother told me you did not take care of her!" *Whack!*

"You are nothing – you hear me?" Kick straight in the abdomen – I could feel the burning and hoped I had not split open. "I hate you, fuckin' Irish whore! When my passport arrives, you are gone!"

He was referring to the fact that the Immigration Officers did spot checks, early morning and late night, to see if we were really living together and it was not just a marriage of convenience for the purpose of acquiring a British passport. I had to stay until he had secured the precious passport.

For the first time I noticed that Mehmet was turned on by beating me. I was on the floor and he was kicking me and whatever way I looked up I noticed his erection! I had believed that the forced sex after each beating was his way of looking for forgiveness. How stupid was I? I realised then that I was not only being abused but raped afterwards! I had never before made the connection! Maybe it was the anger I felt after the surgery that opened my eyes. The only thing this knowledge did was to degrade me further still.

With all the stress my body was enduring, I was not surprised when it began to fight back. My kidney infections were becoming more intense and the pain was unbearable. I was eventually diagnosed with Loin Pain Haematuria Syndrome. I was sure the specialist made it up! All it means is pain in your side and blood in your urine! You have to admit it sounds a bit dodgy. But when I did some research I discovered this condition was very real and the cause was *unknown!*

I could no longer take living in the cell we called home – I often thought about jumping out the third-floor window in my bid to escape. When I could take it no more, I began to beg the council for a flat. I got letters from doctors, social workers, everyone I could think of until eventually I was given a flat in Tulse Hill on health grounds by Lambeth Council in my own name. Unknown to Mehmet, I had been saving up my tips for months to buy things. I told Mehmet that he needed a place to bring people, now that his career was taking off. He had been working his way through the hotel and catering trade. He had just taken a position as manager in a very high-class Turkish restaurant. I used his new-found illusion of grandeur to move out of the cell and into a home. His ego was so big, he fell for it, truly believing he would be entertaining at home!

No expense was spared on furnishings. I tried so hard to make the flat in Tulse Hill a home. But no matter what I bought or did to improve things, behind the door in secret I was still an abused woman!

By April '89 I had finished college and was working as a receptionist in a hotel in Russell Square.

Dr Jones had brought in a few specialists to look at my case and all agreed with the original diagnosis. Only I could have a condition with such a stupid name! I was in severe pain and eating tablets – with no food. I had some tablets called DF118 – I had no idea what they were but I was on them every four hours. I found out later that the tablets were codeine – maybe they helped ease more than the pain in my loin!

By now it was becoming obvious to all that something was very wrong. My weight was plummeting and I looked like hell. Dr Jones decided we should try a procedure called a 'denervation'. The nerves to my troublesome kidney, the left one, would be cut and hopefully I would then be pain-free – I have a feeling he put the weight loss down to stress at that point.

I was admitted during the summer for the operation. I weighed six stone nine pounds! It was at this point Dr Jones became suspicious and questioned me about my eating habits. He contacted my mother and had the nurses watch me. He had no interest in Mehmet and I believe he disliked him.

Once the nurses caught me purge all hell broke loose. I had counsellors and nutritionists trying to get me to admit my eating disorder. I had no idea I had one. Of course, I knew I had a problem with food and I knew in my soul what I was doing was wrong but I would never call it 'an eating disorder' so how the hell could I admit to it? It is not unusual to disbelieve that you are acting out your emotions through an eating disorder and believe me most people would take a long time to admit to it.

During a physical exam Dr Jones discovered the scar from my tummy tuck. Previously I had it hidden by my underwear – as the scar was so low in the abdomen it was easy to hide. I had seldom been examined by Dr Jones himself – it was usually a registrar or house doctor. I felt I had so disappointed him when he saw that I had taken to the knife in order to create the elusive perfect body. I just broke down and told him everything, explaining the bruise on my back was not from a fall, that Mehmet had kicked me.

"Jennifer, you are bulimic anorexic and need help."

"Mehmet wants me thin! What can I do? I want to eat all the time but I can't!"

"The fact you want to eat rules out anorexia as such – yours is more a case of forced starvation. Look, you have to put on weight or the surgery will be cancelled – and worse still you will kill yourself. Jennifer, I know people who will help you. But first you have to admit you have a problem."

"Dr Jones, I am so unhappy. Mehmet hits me – he hates me! But I don't know how to leave him. I am so afraid."

My mother arrived a few days later. The shock on her face when she saw how thin I was made me cry.

My mother wanted me home after the operation. I remember thinking: "She does love me!"

"You have to leave that bastard! Look what he has done to you!"

My mother very seldom swore and I was focusing on 'bastard' for a few seconds in shock. "I don't want to live in Galway, Mam. I know Mehmet is no good but I will stay in London after I leave him. I don't want to go back."

"Why? Everyone cares about you at home and you will be looked after there."

"No, Mam, I don't want to go home! This is my home now. I have a flat and good career prospects. I will leave Mehmet but I want to stay here!"

I had identified Galway as the source of my problems. Mehmet was just a person I met along the way who was, as Helena had said, 'paranoid'. Also, apart from feeding into my self-loathing, he filled my head with unachievable dreams: I was going to live in the high-class section of Turkey. Everyone would respect me! I knew it was bullshit but I also knew going to Galway was not an option.

Mam gave up the fight in exhaustion. She decided that we could talk when I was better.

I had the surgery once I had gained ten pounds. It hurt like hell! I took longer to recover than normal. Dr Jones put this down to my overall health. So I stayed in for three weeks after the operation, to recover fully.

Dr Jones was delighted when I was leaving the hospital – he knew I was off to Ireland the next day. I guess he hoped that he would never see me again – for all the right reasons. Mam had gone home and I know they talked. If I know my mother she told him I would not be coming back, ever!

Mehmet kept well away from the hospital once my secret was discovered. And he took himself off to Turkey for three weeks the day I was discharged! Deep down he was a coward, a good-for-nothing low-life. The problem was, he controlled me so much, could I ever escape?

I went home as planned – to be honest I would rather have stayed in London alone. The pressure in Galway was hell – every member of the family was telling me how to live my life! I argued with my parents regularly. They so wanted to help me and I knew this in my soul, but Mehmet's brainwashing was beginning to take effect and I began to believe his words: 'Your family don't love you – they just want to use you. Look at them! Do you really want to live like them?'.

He was reinforcing the thoughts that were already in my head since childhood.

I knew that the words were harsh – but I was still unstable myself and easily influenced. I was angry and resentful towards my family and no one could convince me to stay. I was sure deep down that all of this was their fault. If they had only seen how unwell I was years ago before I met Mehmet, then I would never have ended up like this. They could have saved me if only they had taken time to listen when I was young. They believed that all my problems were Mehmet's fault, and yes, a great deal were but I had been sick for years, long before Mehmet. I began to hate myself when I was a little girl of eight. I could have been saved then but everyone was far too busy with their own lives to notice. I had built up a form of resentment towards my siblings. All the Christmas and birthday presents meant nothing. I needed hugs and kisses to make me better.

I left under a cloud of disappointment. I had been begged, promised and shouted at but still I left. My life was difficult enough with Mehmet controlling me – no way was I going to let an entire family control me. I believe at this point they gave up on me – I had made my bed and now I must lie in it. I was sure that it was easy for them to give up on me – one problem fewer after all.

9

Mehmet saw my return as a licence to carry on – as normal. So he did! I was beaten, bruised and unloved but I never let the outside world see in.

As well as all the violent abuse, I had also realised that Mehmet was having affairs – and he knew I knew, though we never discussed it. When he was having sex with someone else, he left me alone.

To everyone around us, Mehmet was a respected gentleman and I was his devoted loving wife! How the outside world lapped up the pretence!

I at last was thin enough for people to see me in public. I had moved to Brown's Hotel as a cashier. Both our jobs were shift work and I tried to work opposite shifts to his where possible. If I was not there, he couldn't hurt me. Every Thursday I received my wages into the Halifax and by Friday morning all but twenty-five pounds was direct-debited into Mehmet's account. He controlled everything – my clothes – my make-up (I was now allowed the slightest amount during the winter months but still none at all in summer) – my body – mind – soul – the lot. I was his to do as he pleased with!

That winter was made even more distressing for me by the fact that suddenly my whole family were furious with me because of the outcome of a court case. A family member had lost a compensation case and my parents believed it was my fault. I had been in hospital when the case came to court.

I had witnessed the fall in question over some glasses discarded on steps in a nightclub and I was asked to appear. I was too unwell to travel at the time but I spoke to their solicitor and wrote a statement for them. They won the case first time round and compensation was awarded. This should have been the end of the saga but the amount was appealed and they then lost.

My parents were told the case was lost on appeal due to my absence. My mother was disgusted with me, yet I had done nothing wrong! I received abusive telephone calls from her throughout that winter. I was responsible for the stress they were all suffering due to the court costs they had incurred. Jesus Christ, I was not even in the country! The saga went on for ten months and almost pushed me over the edge. I would sit after a particularly distressing phone call looking at my painkillers and trying to decide if I wanted to go on!

My mother phoned almost every night for a month or so and shouted down the phone at me. "How could you, Jennifer? They could lose the house over what you did!"

"What did I do, Mammy? Nothing, I did nothing!

Why am I always the easy target? It's like the school playground with everyone saying: 'Oh, that's Jennifer's fault!' Next I'll be blamed for World War II – it doesn't matter that I wasn't even born – it was, of course, my fault!"

"Don't you be so smart with me! After what you did, I shouldn't even be talking to you. If you hadn't married that bastard none of this would have happened!"

"What has Mehmet got to do with this?"

"I know he stopped you coming home to help, and now look what's happened!"

"I was in hospital – how could I travel? And help how? Look, I saw the fall and that was it. I told her solicitor what happened over the phone and I wrote a letter for her at the time. They decided to sue and if they lost it's their fault not mine. When are you ever going to believe me? Have you ever stopped to think about the fact that they won first time round with this case? If my presence was so 'very important' and I wasn't there then, how did they win first time?"

"I just don't know any more. I never thought you would turn out like this!"

"Like what?"

"You don't care about your family any more. It's all Mehmet! Look what he has done to you. The man is mad!"

"Look, I am going now. You're not listening to me. Try and see the reality in front of you, Mam. I had nothing to do with them losing the case on appeal. You're acting as if I took to the stand and told the court it was a pack of lies. I was not there, Mam, so how could all this be my fault?"

"I don't know who to believe any more!"

"Goodbye, Mam, I'll ring you tomorrow."

With all this stress added to the normal stresses of my life, it was hardly surprising that I began to get fairly unwell again that winter. By April 1990 the pain in my left kidney was back with a vengeance.

Things were so bad I was admitted at first for pain control. I had not seen Dr Jones since my discharge from the hospital the previous year. When I had reappeared at his clinic six weeks later for a post-operative check-up, he was away. I had left a Galway Crystal vase there for him, which my mother had asked me to give him as a thank-you for looking after me. Now here I was again!

Another battery of tests was ordered and I knew by Dr Jones' face the results were not good.

"I am afraid, Jennifer, the nerves have grown back."

"What now? Can't you just take the kidney out? I have two."

"It's not that simple – I only wish it were. If we removed your left kidney then the right one would have to double in size. You have a congenital defect in that kidney and it would not survive. You would be on the transplant list within a year. And even if there was no congenital problem, this condition can reoccur on the opposite side."

He went on to describe the 'congenital defect' as a 'U-bend' which, while no problem to me normally, could cause serious problems if the other kidney was removed.

This 'U-bend" was a surprise to Dr Jones as much as it was to me! As my problems stemmed from the left kidney, there had been no need for close inspection of the right kidney, at least not until they looked at the possibility of removing one of them.

"So what now? A life on morphine? Can nothing else be done? I need to be strong – you know why – and I can't cope like this." Mehmet used to beat me if I was in pain – he said it annoyed him – I learned to hide any external signs of pain quickly.

"There may be a possibility of other forms of surgery. The kidney itself is working – the damage is in the ducts leading from it to the bladder. There may be an alternative to removing the kidney."

I took up Transcendental Meditation in hospital and discovered I was quite good at it. It was so easy to drift off into a world without pain – I visualised blue skies and soft waves on the shore. My fantasy world was perfect and pain-free.

I was in hospital a few days when Mehmet came in with insurance claim forms. It seems that because I was an NHS patient, my health insurance would pay eighty pounds for every day I was in hospital up to six months – Mehmet wanted it signed over to him! No way was I going to sign that piece of paper for him. I refused.

He closed the curtain and put his hands on my neck. "Sign the form or I will kill you! My life would be better without you anyway!"

"You won't touch me – here in the hospital – you can't!"

"Really?" *Punch!* He hit me hard in the chest.

I let out a scream, I was in so much shock. He'd

actually hit me in public! It was one thing at home in front of his or my family, quite another if others saw him hit me.

"Now sign the form, you fuckin' bitch, or I will do that again! Here! Sign it!"

Just then the curtains were pulled back and in walked one of my doctors.

"What is going on here?"

We could not answer as Mehmet was bending over me – with his hands on my throat! What could he say!

"I would like you to leave the hospital before I call Security – and don't come back!"

Mehmet left with the form unsigned but forged it anyway – he was paid the eighty pounds for each night I stayed in hospital – directly into his account. Considering I was in for three months I believe he made about five thousand pounds out of my suffering.

Dr Jones came in later and just said: "I heard what happened."

I didn't reply and the subject was closed.

I was booked to have a renal auto-transplant on June 29th 1990. It was a new procedure and I was told it had not been done before. I seemed to be a total freak with all my health and mental problems. I was now to be the first person ever to have this surgery! All this only added to my feelings of despair and self-hatred, and almost pushed me over the edge.

My weight was stable by now and I had gained a stone – three stone under what I should have been – but enough to appear as if I was trying to sort myself out.

Mr Young would be my surgeon – I was told he was the best.

I kept expecting to be discharged from hospital – but I then found out I was being kept in for the three months leading up to the surgery!

I was alone! Mehmet was banned from the hospital, I had no friends in London, and my sister Sandra had long ago gone home to Ireland.

I was now totally alone and my family were not interested. From April 10th to July 7th 1990 I sat in the hospital – alone. A social worker arranged for volunteer visitors to come and see me – as well as arranging to claim fifty pounds a week from my stamps so I had money to buy toiletries and a newspaper. The volunteer ladies used to give me toys to sew for the children's ward to keep me busy. I used to bring tea and coffee to the other patients to try and occupy my time.

It was at night I cried – I was about to have an untested operation – I could die – I was so sure no one cared. I had hoped that my family would come over – just a quick visit – but no one came. Mam had spoken to Dr Jones as well as myself and, from the admission in April right through, everyone knew I was in the hospital. It was not as if they had no idea of what was going on.

I had been in control of my bulimia since my last operation. I would eat to live – and if I binged I would purge. I was almost eight stone and still looked like a skeleton! I was broad-shouldered and below my ideal weight – Mehmet convinced me months before this was a good weight for a woman of five foot seven – and I believed him – after all why would he lie to me? I mentioned once after seeing my GP that he felt I should weigh a little more for my height. Mehmet said the weight/height charts in the doctor's surgery were rubbish and I believed him.

Lying in my hospital bed I was thinking about Mehmet and the way he treated me, calling me fat when he used to hit me and using that pet name for me – 'Sisko' – Fatty!

I was so confused about everything I wanted to die all the time.

I knew while I was in hospital he was having a ball. Other women in my bed! I didn't care about him – it was my bed I cared about.

The bulimia began to surface again and in my loneliness I purged. The burning throat once more relieved my pain.

As I sat alone and hurting, waiting for my surgery, I phoned Mehmet at work one night and told him I didn't care what he did but no women were to sleep in my bed. He laughed and put the phone down! I had worked hard to be able to buy that bed; I did not want other women using it.

Sometime in early May I was moved from my ward into High Dependency. I was now on a diamorphine pump and had started having fits – the doctors believed it was stress. Out of the blue I would get the shakes – all over my body. It could last an hour sometimes. I didn't ask many questions – and accepted the diagnosis.

There was a lovely Cypriot woman across from me and we got on really well. She would tell me all about Cyprus and her family. I used to watch the clock for her family's visits as they would talk to me – at times I felt as if I was waiting for my own family to visit.

We went to bed as normal one evening – said the usual 'God Bless' and went to sleep. I was woken about 4 a.m. with the cries of a young woman begging her mother not to die – then I heard it – the 'death rattle'. Fear ran through my veins – I was stuck to my bed, unable to move, frozen with the fear! When I realised it was the Cypriot lady dying I was heartbroken! It went on for hours, then suddenly around 6 a.m. all went quiet – she was gone.

I ran to the phone and called my mother – when she answered I was crying so much it took me ages to get the words out.

"Mammy, please never die – promise me, please!"

"What's happened, Jennifer? Has something happened to you?"

The shock in her voice was obvious – but I had just experienced my first death up close – and all I could think of was my parents – what would I do if they died? I may have run back to Mehmet but I loved my parents deep down, how could I not? Just because I believed that they didn't love me did not mean that I had stopped loving them.

"The lady in my room died! It was awful – I was never so afraid in my life – now all I can think of is you and Daddy. I can't lose you ever – you're not allowed to die on me!"

I had reverted to the mindset of a child – a very frightened one at that. I begged my mother to come and visit me or send someone over – she told me she would try!

Nobody ever came. I was so upset. I was her daughter after all. I knew that Mam was in her mid-sixties and worn out from life but in my distressed state I needed her and she wasn't there.

I settled back into hospital life.

I heard the nurses talking quietly one night.

"Jennifer comes from a big family, doesn't she?"

"According to her notes she's the youngest of nine."

"I wonder why she never has visitors? It's really sad – she's been here for almost three months! Have any of you ever seen her with visitors?"

"No, just the volunteers – you know she's married to a Turkish man – maybe the family don't talk over it?"

"Yeah, but surely when she's so sick they would forget all that and visit the poor girl?"

I went out to them – they were pretty shocked as they thought I was asleep. My bed was behind the nurse's station – they knew I had heard every word!

"Girls, thank you for the concern – but the truth is I have no idea why my family don't visit me – I try every day to work it out – I did nothing to cause it." I couldn't see how my staying with Mehmet or the dispute about the compensation case which was still on-going could have anything to do with my present situation. I was to undergo a huge operation – I could die for Christ's sake! "I know if the tables were turned I would cross many a sea to be with them – I guess I just don't matter."

I burst into tears at this point. One of the nurses took me into the staffroom for a cup of tea and a chat. I went back to bed in tears – there was no sleep for me that night.

Italia '90 passed the month of June for me – there was an

Irish supporter on the ward and we cheered and laughed during the games. Funny, but I was not a football supporter – but in the hospital it became my saving grace – I had something to talk about and someone to talk to.

I passed my days with the tea trolley, going to each patient offering a drink. The little chats and kind smiles of my fellow patients kept me going. I had, after all, nothing else.

All of a sudden it was the night before my surgery – sure I was going to die I began to pray. I believed in angels and prayed to mine for hours – I even sang my signature tune 'Amazing Grace' to them in the hope of surviving my operation. I knew it would be a long one and that I would be out for a couple of days.

I was so frightened that when the nurse and porter came for me that Thursday morning I began to panic – by the time we got to the theatre doors a doctor had to come out and sedate me – my only memory before going under was telling the nurse to tell my parents I loved them.

Next thing I remember it was Friday afternoon and I was in Nuclear Medicine. I knew the room well as I had been there many times before.

I was alive. I began to look at my body. I had tubes everywhere – I counted eight but I knew there were more. I was brought back to High Dependency where I had my own nurse round the clock. She told me the operation was successful. It had taken sixteen and a half hours – I was almost cut in two. My left kidney had been taken out, then reinserted in my right groin in close proximity to my bladder, making new connections between its blood vessels and the arteries and veins there. It was touch and go to get everything working normally.

A priest turned up to offer me the anointing of the sick. I could hardly talk so he went ahead. Knowing I was a Catholic, he felt I would want it. He believed he was helping me – and maybe he did. I could feel the anger inside me turn to strength. I was going to fight this – I knew I had a purpose in life – I just had to find it.

I never thought much about the nurse's statement – "You almost didn't make it" – but I recently received my medical notes and was shocked to see how lucky I was. I had turned blue immediately after my kidney was transplanted – I had organ failure. It took ten minutes to revive and stabilise me! At one point there were almost twenty doctors watching the operation. Medical history was being made and it was my body on the table.

I wonder, if my family had known then what I went through, would anything have changed? I doubt it. My mother had been kept up to date with what was happening but, even with the knowledge of how unwell I was, nobody came. The surgery I had is so rare, even today I have to explain the whole thing to new doctors. The operation was very extreme for the time it took place. I was the first.

I just felt at that time I was an even bigger freak than I had been before the operation. I see from the Internet that there are others now. But it's too late for me. I needed support at the time of my operation and there was none.

10

My mother had arranged for me to go to Ireland when I was discharged from hospital and so I had a phone call two days after my surgery from Dolores. As I was unable to get up, the nurse took a message and wrote it on a yellow card. It read: *"Can you get me a bottle of Beautiful perfume at the Duty Free – love, Dolores."*

I cried like a baby when I read it. I had been hoping it would say 'We love you and are looking forward to seeing you' but Dolores was more concerned with perfume than my health!

My recovery was swift. I think I was so keen to leave what was now my institution that my body recovered in super-quick time. I was out just over a week after my operation. The social worker brought me home to an empty flat – when she saw there was no food she went and did some shopping for me. I spent that first night alone – again. Mehmet had run to Turkey and I was going to Galway a few days later.

I arrived into Galway airport after a very uncomfortable journey – my body ached and I was losing the will to fight. I can't remember who collected me but I know Mam was there. I cried all the tears I had left in my body when I saw her.

"It hurt so much, Mam! I was so lonely!"

"You're home now and I'm going to take care of you."

I was like a child – I was in my mother's arms. I wanted her to take the hurt away. I wanted to be well.

My mother and I had a fractured relationship this time round because of the outcome of that court case. Now my parents seemed to believe that I was actually a bad person. I often remember this time and want so much to scream at the world: "I did nothing wrong!" Their belief only compounded my self-hatred and I was now an unworthy person altogether for something I had *not* done!

The matter was thankfully cleared up. I confronted those involved. Once talk of accessing the case transcript to prove my innocence was introduced, the admission was made that it was not 'really' my fault the case was lost. The truth was, they had won first time round but appealed the award and the fact that it didn't work out had nothing to do with my absence. My name was cleared – sort of – but I carried the pain of my mother disbelieving me for many years. In fact I still do. The scars stayed with me. I was hurt. I never received an apology either from my mother or the other party!

Home was busy as usual. It was July and Mammy had lots of guests staying.

I had expected constant attention but I just seemed to be there. Everyone carried on with their lives as normal. Mam was as usual up to her eyes with the B&B and trying to sort out problems with my sister Mary, whose alcoholism was becoming worse, and her children. I still felt, though, that I should be taken care of. Emotionally, if nothing else.

I wanted to shout: "I could have died! Does anyone care? Maybe I should have died – then you would all be happy!"

Mam had bought me clothes for when I came home. All my life my mother was buying me things: Christmas, birthdays or 'just because'. It was her way of showing she cared but I needed hugs.

Not only was I a medical mess, but my fifteen-year-old niece Sharon who was ill was there, staying with her nana for the weekend. She was in the back bedroom in our house and looked almost dead from Crohn's disease. This is a chronic condition involving severe inflammation of the gastrointestinal tract, causing scarring and thickening of the bowel wall. The doctors had diagnosed she was anorexic for so long before the correct diagnosis was made, the poor child had unduly suffered and was only four stone. I will never forget bathing her, lifting this skeleton in my arms, and the image has never left me. I was recovering from my own surgery but it seemed unimportant when I saw Sharon. I somehow found the strength to look after her. My heart was broken. What happened to me happened because of my eating disorder. I could make peace with that fact but Sharon suffered through no fault of her own. In time she made a recovery and is in remission from her Crohn's disease. She is an adult now, married with the cutest little girl called Katie. She has relapses and remissions but is mostly well these days.

My Aunty Kitty was down from Dublin for the races one afternoon. Sensing my distress, she took me for a walk. We ended up at my brother Andy's house – expecting a cup of tea and a welcome. But Andy was in one of his moods and told us to leave. He came to the door and herded us off his property! Kitty and I were very shaken, having no idea what was going on. We went to Dolores' salon around the corner – I was in tears and Kitty was white as a sheet. We should have been used to his moods by that time as he has been moody all his life but Kitty and I were fragile that day.

I asked Dolores about her perfume request and she just laughed it off. There was no explanation and Lolo knew this so she did what came naturally and laughed.

I remember the joy I felt when I was told that there was a message from my sister. I had prayed it said we love you and get well soon. How hurt I was when I read the note!

If ever there had been a time in my life I needed my family it was then. But I was let down. I was bruised and broken – mentally and physically – and the worst of all this was no one seemed to care. Was I such a bad person? What had I done wrong? I have recalled the pain of that visit so many times with different counsellors and it is always the same. Just recently I went through it all again.

"I tried so hard to be part of the family – yet I seemed to be rejected – why?"

"Maybe, Jennifer, people weren't rejecting you – they were busy with their own lives and children."

"Surely that should not matter – I have always been there for them. Every time there was a problem I was on the end of the phone. I flew home when necessary. Yes, they hated Mehmet but surely the choice of one's mate is not a conditional factor as to one's value in a family? I don't want glory or reward – just acceptance."

"You need to accept that you are important – you deserve to be loved – and if they can't offer you that, I suggest you move on."

I stopped seeing the counsellor when she could not answer my burning questions. I couldn't move on until I understood why I was so unimportant. Even today this hurts me. If I am unwell it is only Honor who comes to my rescue, yet I have two other sisters living right beside me whom I rarely see.

11

When I went back to London I decided not to tell anyone about my life any more – they didn't care so why bother them? My home was London, my flat was there and as to whether my desperation for my own home was the string that tied me to Mehmet, who knows? It was my home and I lived there.

Once everyone knew about my situation – I would often call after a beating and cry down the phone – I needed a friendly ear. I guess I had done it too many times and the family were sick of me. I never asked to be rescued only to be extended a listening ear. It was not a case of 'Save me, please!'. I would call and talk about what had happened, always saying I would one day leave but not then. Whatever the reason for their lack of interest in me, I know I would never abandon any of them no matter what was happening in their lives. Maybe I just expected too much or I was not good enough to be loved?

Mehmet came back to London soon after I returned

and he brought me an STD – a Sexually Transmitted Disease! When I told him he beat me!

Life returned to whatever normal was. I got a job in the Café Royal and was never so happy. I loved my job and the excitement it brought me: I could have been hit at home in the morning and greeting Princess Diana in the evening. We never actually spoke to her, just bowed as she came in – I fantasised about conversations we would have about our eating disorders – I was still an active bulimic. She was not very beautiful when you saw her in the flesh but she had the most beautiful presence about her.

For the next year life went on. Nothing really changed at home – I seldom saw Mehmet. As reception manager, I did the timetables for all the front-of-house staff and where possible I worked the opposite of Mehmet's shifts.

That Christmas we had the Vienna Boys' Choir perform in Reception – I phoned my mother and left the phone on the reception desk so she could listen. I knew she loved them – and that night she listened to the whole concert on the phone.

As usual Mehmet went to Turkey for Christmas and New Year – I was happy to be alone in my little flat in Tulse Hill. But Christmas Day was very hard for me. I sat in the lounge eating a ready-made meal watching the telly. I was so lonely inside I ached from head to toe.

Later that afternoon I had one of my strange fits and had the emergency doctors out. They were saddened by my situation, all alone on Christmas Day. I would have these fits every so often. No one could say what they were, panic attacks or a disease of the nervous system. I had no intention of finding out what caused them. I'd had enough of hospitals and with time the fits passed.

When Mehmet returned he brought with him the worst news possible. His mother was coming for another holiday. I wanted to get sick. When she arrived I had to pretend to welcome her – knowing what would happen if I didn't.

Mehmet worked all-day shifts during her visit – and of course I worked nights. I stayed in my room during the day for as long as possible – I had no intention of entertaining her. I gave her breakfast, lunch and cups of tea; Mehmet arranged dinner. Every time I watched her eat I wished she would choke! She was a big fat round lump who made me suffer and I hated her.

I had been phoning home quite a bit during Sebahat's visit, needing support, though I had stopped telling them about Mehmet's abuse. When the bill came I hid it in my pocket. I had no idea how I was going to pay the two hundred and twenty-five pounds! Mehmet took my wages every week and I was in an awful dilemma. There were no tips any more – I was panicking. One evening the asshole noticed the bill in my jeans pocket – I had been sitting and when I got up a bit was poking out. I had kept it with me at all times since it arrived, hoping he would never find it. My plan was to ask him for the usual cheque of a hundred and twenty or so and make the rest up with my weekly money. If I bought the necessities such as shampoo in the market I was sure I could do it in six weeks. He took the bill and it began. He told his mother how much it was and she began to criticise me. She said I spent all day in bed – on the phone.

"You fuckin' bitch, spending my money talking to

your no-good family!" *Whack!* "I will fuckin' show you – you whore!" *Kick!*

I looked at his mother – she was watching her son hit me – yet she did nothing! I was on the sitting-room floor. When he stopped to tell his mother what a bad wife I was, I ran to the bedroom.

He followed and threw me on the bed – and began to strangle me – all the while saying: "You bitch, I hate you – die, you fuckin' bitch – I hate you!"

As I felt my life drain out of my body, I did not fear death – I had so long wished it. My only regret was that I would never have a child – or be a grandmother. Just as I was about to pass out, I heard his mother's voice.

"Stop, Mehmet! You will go to prison – she's not worth it!"

I had a good understanding of Turkish by then and I was shocked that her only concern was her son – and not the innocent woman he was killing! He stopped, punched my face, then called me a whore.

We did not speak for over a week – any of us. Mehmet was definitely sick – he sat with his mother like a child – he spoke with the voice of a child and sat on the floor with his head in her lap! He was thirty-seven at the time. Whatever problems I had, his were much worse.

Eventually she went home and I could relax again. She had taken over my home – I found bits of her everywhere! While they went to the airport I reclaimed my territory.

I went to Ireland in May for my niece Tracy's First Communion. My mother had taken my sister Mary's children to live with her. Mam and Dad had tried everything to help Mary but she always went back on the bottle, so the three girls went to live with their nana. They were much happier and my mother wanted to make a fuss of the Communion so I went home as requested.

Lolo was living in Spain by then, having retired from hairdressing. I used to think how lucky she and Douglas were to have so much money they could just sell up and retire. They were only in their mid-to-late thirties at the time.

It was a lovely day and Mary seemed sober. Tracy looked beautiful. I had been away during all the commotion so knew very little about Mary's situation. I hardly knew her and only heard about her problems second-hand. She seemed happy enough with her life, I thought. She was trying to stay sober again, she had a new home and the children were slowly beginning to live with her again. She had met this guy who appeared to look after her – her marriage had ended years before.

Later that evening there was a phone call to our house: Mary was drinking again. I went with my sister to take the two children, who had been staying with her for the weekend, back to our mother's. I felt so sorry for everyone when I saw how drunk my sister was and how afraid the children were. This was the first time I witnessed Mary in this state. We went home, got the kids to bed and carried on as normal.

There was another phone call the following afternoon: one that would change our lives forever. Mary had been driving drunk and hit a man on the road. The man had died! Mary was too drunk to arrest so the gardai brought her home. Mammy was distraught. One of her children was in trouble with the police! She had always been so proud that none of us had got into trouble or broken the law – now she was faced with the worst offence she could ever imagine. I went to Mary's flat to check on her with Honor and she had no idea what had happened. Mary believed she had hit a wall! I never drank very much and even my dalliance with cannabis had never led to harm of any kind. Alcoholism was new to me and it scared me. I could not imagine wanting a drink so badly that nothing else mattered! I was not an alcoholic; the addiction seemed ridiculous to me until I looked at my own life. I was addicted to my eating disorder! The comfort I received from purging in some way resembled Mary's comfort from alcohol! I felt so sorry for her yet I said nothing – how could I?

The whole family was in shock. We sat and drank tea most of the night. Mammy would cry every now and then and Daddy sat in shame and silence. The following morning the mood remained the same.

I remember speaking to my parents about the accident.

"Look, Mary has a sickness and everyone knows about it – you have nothing to be ashamed of."

"Of course, we have! She is our daughter. Your father and I tried everything to help her. Why did she do this?"

"Mammy, Mary has no idea she did anything."

"And that alone makes it worse! How can we ever show our faces in public again, knowing what our Mary did?"

"Everyone knows it's not your fault. You were not driving the car, remember! You know what? Neither was Mary. Not the Mary you raised but the Mary whose life is so dependent on alcohol it is all she can think about."

Mammy cried again.

I had to get back to work a couple of days later. I hated leaving my parents to face this and wished I could have helped. I hugged and kissed them both like never before the morning I was leaving. I told them I loved and respected them so much but they were too shocked to respond.

I was no sooner a week back when my brother Andy phoned on Saturday evening June 8th 1991 – I will never forget the date as long as I live.

"Jennifer, you have to come home – Mammy's had a stroke."

"She couldn't have. I was speaking to her two hours ago and all was fine until she said she had a headache and had to go."

"She rang my house after that for Daddy to come home – when we got there she had collapsed."

"Jesus Christ, no! Not Mammy!"

"Look, she's in a coma and the father is a mess. Just get home."

"I'll be there as soon as I can. Andy, tell her I love her and I am on my way home. Just in case."

"I will. Now stop talking and get home. You can tell her yourself then."

Andy was always great in a crisis. He had a way of getting things done. He was also the one you were most likely to fall out with in the family. Andy is quick-tempered and believes his way is always the right way. If you disagree, he won't talk to you. It's that simple.

Mehmet was at home when I got the call – he handed me his credit card. Shocked at his kindness, my only concern was a flight home. I managed to book a seat on the first flight into Galway Sunday morning. Then I sat all night in the chair. Mehmet left me in my silence. I was in shock and could not speak to him – all I wanted was to be in Ireland. I remember thinking if only we had transporters like they do on *Star Trek*! How strange the thoughts that flow through the mind, in times of distress.

Soon it was morning and the heavy lull of night had lifted. I had nothing prepared for my journey and had to move fast. I only had a couple of hours to get to the airport. I threw everything I could see into my suitcase and hoped for the best. I made it to the airport with ten minutes to spare for check-in.

As usual I was alone. With my ticket in my hand I began to make my way to the gate. It was then reality hit me. I could lose my mother today! We had so many unresolved issues, she might never be able to tell me she loved me and I might not have the chance to explain how I felt!

"Dear God, please let me have time with my mother! Please don't take her away from me, not yet, please, God!"

I prayed all the way to the plane with tears running down my face. I knew people were looking at me and I couldn't care less. I knew I was going home to say goodbye to my mother. All I needed was a little time to explain.

12

I cried all the way to Galway, for myself as much as my mother. I'd had so much pain in my life so far, I was sure I could take no more. My cousin John met me off the plane and reassured me all the way to the hospital that everything would be OK. I knew he was saying what he thought I needed to hear, that's what everyone does in a crisis. I wanted the truth. I already knew Mammy would die but I wanted to hear it from the doctor's mouth.

There is something strange about hospital corridors – the faint light, and the sound of your feet as you walk. I felt like I was walking forever when I saw my father – his white hair and navy coat. He stood tall and strong, only his face belied this impression. I knew when I saw him the news was bad. I ran to Daddy as a child would after a fall – I needed to be reassured that everything would be fine – the hurt would go away.

"Daddy, what's happened?"

"I don't know. They think your mother had a brain

haemorrhage. We have to wait and see what happens for now."

"Where is she? I need to see her!"

"The first bed on the right. You have to be quiet – the other patients are trying to eat their lunch. Don't make a scene."

What a strange thing to say! His wife is dying and yet he is concerned for others! Daddy didn't do drama. Always the quiet man.

I stood for a moment before I opened the curtains around the bed. The light was on and sitting holding Mammy's hand was Honor – I was trying so hard not to look down at the bed, fearful of what awaited me.

What I saw was surprisingly calm. My mother, no more than five foot two, lay sleeping, her blonde hair perfectly combed and her wrinkle-free face belying her age – she looked like a child in a deep sleep waiting for morning to come.

I went and sat by the bed. It was then the tubes reminded me we were in hospital. Honor and I looked at each other with tears welling. As my mother lay in her coma she had on either side her oldest and youngest daughters. We sat quietly for a while, then went to the corridor and cried openly, surrounded by the family.

Andy was in organisation mode. So far he had been unable to contact all the family. Gabrielle was over for a holiday with Dolores on the Costa del Sol and it was quite possible that they were away somewhere. Andy kept trying. Brian was on some Spanish island. He had been out when Andy phoned and didn't receive his message to call home until the Saturday night.

We all stayed in the hospital well into the night until

we decided that we would take shifts staying by Mammy's bed until she came back to us.

The house was strange. I had not been there since I arrived home. The air was still and I was sure a dark cloud hung over us. Mammy should be here in her kitchen drinking her strong tea and chatting. I stood at the kitchen door as Honor put the kettle on – I waited at the door, not wanting to go in, for as soon as I did I would know Mammy was not there. Her chair was empty, she was gone.

Andy and Honor had been to the Garda Station and Interpol had been asked to try and locate Dolores and Gabrielle. As the two of them arrived back to Dolores' house after the weekend away, the police car was in the drive. They managed to get a flight on Monday morning. Brian was not so lucky – every plane was full. I remember clearly Gabrielle and Dolores arriving at the hospital. We heard the click-click of Dolores' shoes before we saw her. The sound of her heels being so familiar to us, we all knew they had arrived as soon as we heard the noise.

A number of doctors came and went during Monday, often stopping outside the ward to confer. All we could hear was muttered tones until eventually one of them asked to speak to Daddy. Mammy was being sent to Dublin the following day. The Beaumont specialised in head injuries and she was to be taken by helicopter, so urgent was her case. The coma was as a result of her haemorrhage – if anyone could help her it would be the doctors in the Beaumont.

So the following morning we all went to the hospital

and waved her off on her journey. We would all follow in cars. I have no idea who I went with – I just know I got there that evening.

Once more we collected in a hospital corridor. I counted thirteen of us at one stage. Information was scarce as new tests were needed – the Beaumont had bigger and better machines than Galway and once the tests were done we would be told the prognosis.

My cousin Paul and his wife Irene lived near the hospital and opened their doors to the family in our time of need. I have no idea how they put up with the invasion but not once did they complain. We slept on any available spot and were fed and watered for the duration of our stay. I will never forget their kindness.

Mammy kept slipping in and out of her coma. She would partially wake up sometimes as if she were coming out of a deep sleep, mutter something and she was gone. At times our hopes were raised and we spoke to her but a couple of hours later she would be gone again. This went on all week and her neurosurgeon was waiting for her to wake up fully as it was too dangerous to administer an anaesthetic with her like this.

We began to believe that we would take Mammy home. The air around us was lighter; the once glum faces were now replaced with hope.

My twenty-sixth birthday was on Tuesday 13th of June and Mam sang 'Happy Birthday' to me on the Monday! I was filled with pride and told anyone who would listen. Honor and I had arrived at the hospital that afternoon and Mam was sitting up having a cup of tea! We knew for sure that this was it. She had come back to us. Later that day my brother Brian arrived back in

Ireland and I believe that when he went to the hospital Mammy was chatting away. I had gone back to Paul's house by the time Brian arrived.

In Paul's house that night we laughed and chatted as if everything was OK. When Dad came in, he too was lighter and looking forward to the future.

The surgery was planned for the Tuesday morning and we were told not to come to the hospital until after lunch. I was sure because the surgery was on my birthday that everything would be all right. It was a good omen. The whole family went to Mass that morning and prayed that all was going well. We were a bit unnerved by the fact that the Mass was also a Funeral Mass. You could see Daddy visibly shake when he realised.

Dolores arrived at the church with the usual click-click of heels. We thought she was joining us for Mass. She had come to tell us the operation was cancelled! Mam was back in a coma.

We all left the church and made our way to the hospital. Honor and I were first down the corridor as usual. A nurse took us to one side to explain. Mam had not gone to surgery – she had gone back into a coma the night before.

I was dumbstruck when I saw her and had one of my fits which we figured was a panic attack. A doctor was called to help me and the rest is a blur. I knew that Mam went to theatre to have a hole bored in her head to relieve the pressure on her brain. I felt nothing. I was in shock.

The next time I went to the hospital Mam was in Intensive Care and on life-support. I had not had the chance to talk to her! I had to do it not knowing if she could hear or understand what I was saying.

"I am so sorry, Mammy. I know you loved me but I was too sick to understand. I wanted you all to myself and when it didn't happen I thought you didn't love me!"

The machine hissed away in the background as I tried to fix things with my mother.

"Please, Mam, forgive me? I don't know why I am like this. I do love you with all my heart. I am so sorry I didn't show you and now it's too late!"

I cried bitter tears as I held her cold lifeless hand in mine. What a pitiful sight it must have been!

"Please don't die, Mam, please! How will I cope?"

I was shocked to hear myself say the words! Here I was as my mother lay dying, thinking about myself. My self-hatred was only deepened by my actions!

Mr Phillips, my mother's consultant, gathered the family in a side room. We were told that Mam had a congenital aneurysm and that there was evidence of small bleeds in the past.

In unison we began to declare: "Remember when Mam forgot who we were?" and "What about the time she broke her hip? She had no idea how it happened!"

Mr Phillips continued. "We have done all we can for Maureen. We can do nothing more. Her brain is dying and I am sorry to say but it is only a matter of time."

You could tell this was not his first time delivering devastating news to people. Just the right amount of kindness and sincerity. I wondered how he did his job.

I went into the room and said a tearful goodbye to my mother – I swore that I would become a better person.

I could not believe how well Dad was coping. Then I went to his room in Paul's that night and found him crying with his head in his hands.

"How are we going to cope without her, Dad?"

"I don't know – I just don't know!"

"I love you and I am here if you need me."

"Thanks."

I left him to his tears, knowing that this private man needed time to cry alone.

The following morning I ran back to Galway, not wanting to be present for the final moments. I had said my goodbye on the Friday night and now I had to run. I seemed to always be running from something only this time it was my mother's death.

I had this memory in my mind as I travelled back to Galway with Sandra and Christy on the early train. All I could say was "Poor Daddy!". He had to overcome this and we could do nothing to help him.

Sandra and Christy had moved home over a year before and were now living in the same street as my parents. We were to prepare things for the funeral we knew was coming. I was so relieved to have left the hospital and not be present when Mam died that I could not wait to be home in the familiar kitchen.

I had a major fight with Sandra back at the house. The only empty room was my parents and no way was I sleeping in my mother's bed!

"It's the only empty room in the house," said Sandra. "You are not sleeping on the sofa. I have the place clean for when Dad comes home!"

"Sandra, if you think I am sleeping in Mammy's bed you have another think coming. I am sleeping here. Look, I will clean up in the morning."

"You are *not* sleeping on the sofa! Now get up to bed!"

I was incensed that Sandra thought she could tell me what to do! Who the hell did she think she was?

"I am sleeping here and, if you don't like it, tough shit! Now feck off and leave me alone!"

We went on like this for hours, both struggling with our grief and taking our anger out on each other. I slept on the sofa, too fearful to spend the night in my parents' bed. What if she died in the night and her sprit came to the room?

I went to midday Mass on Sunday and just as the choir began to sing 'Amazing Grace' I knew she was dead. I cried the tears of a lost child with half the church looking at me. She was gone. I felt helpless.

Mammy was coming home in a coffin on the Monday and we were all deflated. Fifteen days we had prayed and hoped and now we had to bury her. Andy's wife Mary and I were given the task of bringing the clothes to the funeral home. I was obsessed with underwear – no way was my mother being buried without them. I pulled out drawers and wardrobes until I found what I knew she would like. Off we went with the red dress Daddy wanted and the underwear. I felt I was doing something good – I was proud to help. But Mam's coffin was no sooner in the funeral home when the Blame Game began. Half the town were talking and the consensus was clear: Mary had caused my mother's death. I felt confused by this conclusion but went along with it anyway. I couldn't help thinking Mam's time was up and what had happened with Mary had little to do with her death. We were told how lucky we were she had lived so long with the aneurysm. In fact her Valium may have helped by keeping her blood pressure down. This was fate. Her time with us was up. It was time she had a break from life. I had a niggling feeling that if we were to blame Mary then we should blame ourselves, all of us.

I was told that evening that I was singing at the funeral! Daddy wanted me to sing 'Amazing Grace' as I had so many times before. When Andy told me, I was shocked to say the least.

"You're not serious! Sing at the funeral?"

"It's what the mother would have wanted."

"I'll break down and make a mess in front of everyone!"

"Do it for the father then. You're doing it. It's what they both want."

I wanted to kill Andy.

The following day when I went to the school to practise with the choir, I somehow found my voice and arranged with Sister Breda that, if I felt unable to sing at any time during the hymn, I would just raise my hand and the choir would take over.

I can't remember anything other than standing in the funeral home staring at my mother dead in a coffin! The lid went on and I wanted to die on the spot – I had nothing left to live for!

I took to the altar the following morning and sang my heart out. A couple of hours before, Aunty Kitty was worried I would not be able to sing as I kept crying. Somehow I did it. I said goodbye in song.

13

I had to get back to work in the Café Royal – they had phoned a few times as I was away so long. In fact I found them rather insensitive about the whole episode. I forgave them when I saw the beautiful flowers they sent for my mother. I went back to London and couldn't care less about my life.

Mehmet was taking me to Turkey to meet his family! After the British passport arrived, I had hoped he would leave but by then I was an asset – I earned good money and had gained social status among his friends. I no more wanted to meet this fecker's family but I agreed to go anyway.

Then I was at work one Friday and just lost it. I think I had a mini-breakdown. I cried snotty tears and decided to go back to Galway to be with my father. I went to Personnel.

"I have to leave – I need to be with my father."

"Are you sure, Jennifer? Take a few days to think about it."

"No, I have to go as soon as possible. I need to be in Ireland."

And so I left the job I loved so much. I was going home, leaving Mehmet go to Turkey alone.

I waited until he came in from work.

"I am going to Galway in the morning. I need to be with my father."

"What about your job?"

"I left this afternoon."

I watched the anger rise within him – I knew what was coming next.

"You stupid fuckin' bitch! How could you leave your job without my permission?"

"Mehmet, I really don't care! Beat me if it makes you feel better – you can't hurt me – I am in too much pain already."

"I should have left you when I got the passport! I stayed to help you and now you are making a fool of me!"

"How could I be making a fool of you? In any case, I left the job and I am going home – in fact I may never come back."

He just went off to bed without another word. I was shocked that he gave in so easily. Maybe he'd decided I was not worth it or that I would explode if he beat me. I knew I looked like a madwoman! I had cried so much my face was pure white and my hair was a mess. For once, maybe he feared me?

I left the next day, promising to meet him in Istanbul. I had my ticket and he was sure I would go to Turkey and not let him down but at that moment I had no feelings for anyone but myself.

Galway was not what I expected – no one was interested in me, or my feelings. I so needed to be healed and I thought at the time I had to be in the family house to do this. They were all too busy with their own affairs. As if to add to my despair, I was informed that Tom, the old man that lived with my parents, had told my father that I was fighting on the phone with my mother when she had the haemorrhage! He came up with a tale of how I was telling her I had been beaten the night before. He told Dad that Mammy was shouting at me to leave Mehmet and come home when she grabbed her head and fell. The stupid fool had been trying to get attention or something. I had been on the phone to my mother before she had her haemorrhage chatting as normal, no drama or argument. The call was about my sister Mary who was in Rehab. Andy was due to visit the following day and Mam was wondering how Mary was doing. My mother had phoned Andy's house after speaking to me, to ask my dad to come back to the house. Tom's tale was lies. He probably made them up to get back at me for never liking him or something. He was now a mean vindictive old man – he had got worse with age. I could have strangled the old bastard when I heard what had been said. I just let it be – what was the point? I never spoke to Tom again and he died about four years after my mother. I didn't care. He had been hell for Honor in his final years, always accusing her of flooding his bedroom and other such fantasies. He had become senile with age and it seemed strange that this man with no family had outlived my mother who had so many who wanted her.

I was wondering in bed one night what made me believe coming home would help? I was an outsider here; I fitted in nowhere. My father was gone with Andy almost every day and when he was home I had no idea how to talk to him. My father was dying inside. Losing the woman he loved had broken him – Daddy had no strength to fix me. I had hoped that by tackling our grief together we could heal each other. I was wrong.

I decided to go to Turkey and all hell broke loose. I was told I was not going! Suddenly everyone thought they could control me! I was told I was to stay in Ireland and help look after my father! I was incapable of looking after myself so how the hell could I help Daddy? Honor was there for Daddy now and he seemed happy with the arrangement. Why would he want me? I was, after all, worthless.

The fights went on and I decided life with Mehmet was better than here – I could cope with one person trying to control me but not my whole family. They believed by bullying me they could convince me to stay! I would only run when bullied but they did not know me so how could they know this? I'd had enough bullying in my life and one was a better option than eight. I knew with Mehmet I would have reprieves when he worked or went to Turkey – at home they would all be there all the time to tell me what to do.

One cannot begin to understand my mindset at that time unless one has been in a similar situation, or has an understanding of Battered Woman Syndrome. I was being asked by a family I was sure didn't love me to leave a man who said he did. I forgave each rape and beating as so many others do. I believed the promises of a wonderful life with Mehmet. I was seeking happiness at any cost.

For my father's sake and to stop the fighting I agreed not to go to Turkey and to stay a few weeks longer in Galway.

I also decided without any real forethought that the only unconditional love I would ever have would be from a child. I dumped my packets of the Pill the next day. It was a sudden and bad decision but I felt it was the only thing I could do to be worth something in this world.

I phoned Mehmet's nephew to tell him I was not going to Istanbul. I decided to stay with my father for a bit, but by Jesus I was going back to London! The stupid fool of a nephew never passed on the message and I received an angry phone call from Mehmet.

"Where are you? Why did you not come?"

"Well, I am speaking on the phone in Dad's house so I guess I am at home in Galway."

"You are making a fool of me, you bitch!"

"Tell people my father took a turn and I had to stay in Ireland. Is that so difficult?"

"It's too late now – everyone was waiting to meet you and you make a fucking fool of me like this! How dare you?"

"Look, I am going back to London in two weeks but now I have to stay here."

"I will not go back. I never want to see you again, you whore!"

"Fine."

I put the phone down. I know he was shocked that I, Jennifer, was talking back! The weak fat girl had a voice and dared to disobey Mehmet! I had a feeling of satisfaction that he had waited at the airport for me and I did not show, just as he had done to me four years earlier.

My bulimia was rampant throughout this whole period. I

was getting a bit too thin again and I began to be careful. I needed the purge to heal my pain but I made sure my stomach was empty. I began to allow the one meal I ate a day to digest. I was maintaining my weight at around nine stone maximum but I still managed to inflict the pain I needed to survive.

I returned to my flat in Tulse Hill, alone as usual. I left behind my father, so broken that he begged death to come and take him to his Maureen. I could not imagine what it would be like to love another person so much that the pain of losing them was unbearable. I wished that Mehmet would die most days, believing that I would be free to live then. And the next day if he was nice to me I felt awful for even thinking it.

Mehmet returned to London knowing that I had changed. I was filled with anger and ready to blow. For a couple of months he used only insults to drag me down – he knew if he hit me I would retaliate.

I kept in touch with Women's Aid. Paul was long gone but I phoned every week and discussed what I would do when I left Mehmet. Slowly my 'run money' in my secret account was building up, waiting for me when I needed it.

I did not go back to work when I returned to London – instead I claimed income support from my stamps.

I was now a 'lazy fuckin' fat bitch'.

Every day it was the same. I was insulted as Mehmet got ready for work. He was becoming more and more pissed off that he had lost my income – no point in taking my forty-nine pounds a week. To him it was useless money and he knew I knew this.

I made no effort to get a job.

"You lazy fuckin' bitch! Get up off your fat arse and work!"

"I am still not ready to work and there is nothing you can do about it."

"You make me sick! I hate you! I am leaving and you can sit here and eat – no one will ever want you – you are nothing – nothing!"

"Just go to work and leave me alone – leave if you want – I couldn't care less."

He went for his slipper but thought better of it. I was capable of killing him and he knew it.

I went home for the first Christmas after my mother's death. I was worried about how Dad would get through it. Christmas was always a very big event in our house.

But not this time. My sister Mary was found guilty of causing death by dangerous driving and given a custodial sentence. We tried to keep the newspaper away from Dad. It was Christmas Eve and Mary's trial took up a few pages. We knew it would destroy Daddy to see it. But he did see the paper before the day was out and you could see the pain in his face. A proud man who had raised his children to respect the law, and now his daughter was being sent to prison! I was raging with the courts. You don't send an alcoholic to prison! You send them to rehab. Mary needed help not punishment; every day of her life was punishment enough. Why did they not help her? Twelve months in Rehab would surely give her a chance to recover. I was sure it was the answer, but I did not understand alcoholism. Mary could spend five years in rehab and still go back to drink. She was a chronic alcoholic and maybe just a little too far gone for help. Her life must have been so painful but nothing could be done. It had all been done already to no avail.

Everyone who knew the family was aware of Mary's long-term alcoholism and my father received only sympathy and respect from his friends and neighbours. Still nothing made the matter easier for him to bear.

Christmas was a washout. Everyone tried but we could not celebrate. Our grief was still too raw.

I went back to London in the New Year and just carried on as before.

When I found no solace in Galway I had decided to have a child instead. I wanted a child for all the wrong reasons but went ahead anyway.

Back in London, I fell pregnant. I waited until Mehmet was in a good mood one evening and told him. His reaction was far worse than I could ever have imagined.

"Mehmet, I did a test today and guess what? I am pregnant!"

It took a few minutes for a reply to come and it was nothing like what I was hoping for.

"If you think I am allowing you – you fuckin' good-for-nothing whore – to have *my* child you are very wrong! Tomorrow I will make the appointment and get rid of it. You will not have *my* child, you hear me?"

"I will not have an abortion and you can't make me ever. This is *my* baby, not yours – all you did was lend a sperm. It's nothing to do with you and never will be!"

My bravery was about to be dashed in the cruellest way. Mehmet stood up from the chair and he was like a madman. All the weeks of suppressed anger were about to boil over and I was his target.

"You will not disrespect me, you hear?" *Whack!* Straight in the face.

"Mehmet, please don't! I am pregnant – please don't hit me! You will hurt the baby!"

"Like I give a fuck! I will kick the bastard out of you!"

"Please, Mehmet, please, I am begging you! I will go away and you will never hear from me again – I won't tell anyone the baby is yours!"

This only angered him more and he kicked at my stomach like it was a football. He stamped on my feet so hard he broke three of my toes.

Two days later I found myself in the A&E at University College Hospital. The baby was gone! So was the little bit of strength I had built up since my mother died. I was an empty shell again and he was back in control.

Was I ever going to be loved in this life? I felt so empty and sad, I had been sure a child would make my life complete. My nose was broken but I declined a repair, not wanting to suffer the pain again. To be honest, I didn't really feel it at the time it broke. I was too worried about the baby. I never even noticed until afterwards. To this day the right side of my nose slants inwards.

Once I knew the baby was gone everything hurt so bad I wanted to faint. Mehmet won't be so lucky next time, I thought – he will need his sexual release and the next time I get pregnant I will run.

I was grieving for two people when Mehmet told me we were moving to Coventry. He had arranged for us to manage a hotel there. The owner just needed to meet me before issuing the contracts. I went to the interview in professional mode and the arrangement was confirmed. I would work five or six days a week and return to London on my days off. I knew how the industry worked and was aware that we would not only run the place but work twenty-hour shifts if needed. If someone doesn't turn up for work, as the manager you have to do their job, whatever it may be. Mehmet didn't realise this and it came as a shock! He would make me do the work on his shifts. I was working eighty to ninety hours a week, while the bastard only worked about sixty. I was always called on when staff on his shift didn't turn up. He wouldn't get his hands dirty! Mehmet was a food and beverage manager and the position had gone to his already big head.

We went on like this for months until one morning while trying to cook and serve breakfast my body gave up. I collapsed and was taken to hospital. When the General Manager found out about my health problems, Mehmet used me as an excuse to get out of the contract.

We went back to London and he returned to the Turkish restaurant looking for his job back. He was taken back, only this time he was not manager. He had been replaced.

Mehmet found taking orders too hard and talked about moving to Istanbul where life would be better for everyone. Including me! With his puppet back in the frame I was once again useful! The three floors of an apartment block 'we' were paying for in Turkey were almost complete.

Arrangements were made. He began applying for jobs and was soon successful – Mehmet always believed his own importance and now he was going back to Turkey with a managerial job in one of the world's biggest hotel chains.

The move was on. We would rent my flat and go start a new life. I just agreed with everything, knowing deep inside it was wrong, but what else could I do? My family were not interested so why the hell should I be? The only person I ever heard from was Honor and most of the time it was I who called Gabrielle. I never heard from Dolores unless her husband wanted me to get him some computer part or something. There were no 'Hi, how are you?' calls for me.

But I still had my fantasy family to comfort me in the darkest moments. They were my saving grace on many a bad night and kept me sane throughout my living hell. If only they were real! What a life I would have!

I still hadn't gone back to taking the Pill and I'd had another miscarriage after another beating. I hadn't bothered telling Mehmet about the pregnancy. As if he gave a shit – if he had known he would have only tried to beat it out of me anyway. After that I began to take the Pill again.

I had begun going to different A&E departments with my injuries over the years to try and keep my problems secret. I gave false names made up on the spot. To be honest I don't even remember who I was supposed to be!

I had my toes broken for the second time when he stamped on my feet one morning because I was in his way! I avoided St Thomas' Hospital as I did not want the doctors knowing I was still being abused so I went to King's College A&E instead. I made up stories but of course the doctors knew – they had seen it all before. As bad as things were, this was my life now and I was resigned to it. Mehmet's secret was safe. False names and made-up national insurance numbers. No one would ever know he was a wife-beater – except Sebahat!

14

At Heathrow, waiting for my flight was a surreal experience. I seemed to always be at airports but this time Mehmet was with me. He was so excited about going home to his mammy he had his arm around my shoulders! He went so far as to kiss me a few times while we waited! I was confused. This show of affection in public made me wonder what lay ahead. Was my new life going to be one of respect rather than hatred? Only time would tell. I think deep down Mehmet had feelings for me but what they were was anyone's guess. Certainly not love.

I had never seen this man so excited in my life as the plane took off! He sat there with a huge smile, telling all around him about his new life while I spent the three hours in my head with my fantasy family. Once we landed we had to deal with Immigration. Mehmet had registered me as a Turkish citizen and even though I had my papers we still had to pay for something else related to my entry. I knew a lot of Turkish by this time. I may have had grammar problems but I understood what was being said.

His brother was waiting for us and Mehmet had a tearful welcome home. I was beginning to form opinions of Turkish culture. The men were forever devoted to the mother and siblings yet behaved violently with their wives. I had learned this from all the other wives I had spoken to in London.

I went to his mother's house under the promise that as soon as the apartment was ready we would move. Mehmet's brother and mother lived in the same apartment block and it was his brother's wife Dalma who helped me through the six weeks of living with my mother-in-law! I thanked God many times during those early days that I had decided to learn to speak Turkish, otherwise I would have been unable to communicate and have my chats with Damla.

I discovered that Sebahat was the bitch I believed her to be and her daughter-in-law wished her dead. One afternoon Damla and I chatted about Sebahat while sitting in the sun.

"She is a horrible woman, and bad minded." she said.

"Why do Mehmet and Mert behave like babies when they are with her?"

"This is the way she likes it. I promise you, Jennifer, she will make sure you know that she comes first. Mehmet is her son and you are just his wife – there to give her a grandson she will keep for herself!"

"What do you mean?"

"Once my son Hakan was born, she took over. He was her grandson; I was only his mother. Even now he loves her more than me and she loves watching me hurt. Watch them this evening at dinner."

"What about the other kids?"

"They have no importance and this hurts them. My daughters are nothing to her. I have three children but it is her grandson who she loves most."

Taking my chance, I asked the burning question. "Does Mert ever hit you?"

"Hit me? Oh yes, he loved to hit me when we were younger, then he would run upstairs to her and she would shout at me for upsetting her son."

"What about now? Mehmet hits me whenever he feels like it – everything is my fault."

"It was exactly the same for me. The only break I got was when I was pregnant."

"Mehmet beat a baby out of me once! He doesn't want me to carry his child!"

"Mehmet is too selfish to be a father – he always has been. But she will want his child – once the house is ready she will start asking him. You will see."

"Damla, why do you stay?"

"For the same reason as you – it is my destiny. I don't love Mert, not even when we married – but the match was made and I had to honour it."

I watched that evening as Sebahat put her arms around Hakan and held him close. He was nineteen and she held him like a baby, as her granddaughters sat and watched. Just as Damla said, he came home, kissed his mother, then sat holding his gran for the rest of the evening.

Religion had never been discussed between Mehmet and me but I could see Mehmet's family were religious and prayed five times a day. Mehmet had never prayed as far as I knew but suddenly I was being questioned about my beliefs! Sebahat would tell me any children must be

Muslim and not Catholic. I just sat there and said nothing.

The apartment was almost ready and I was becoming impatient, wanting to have my own home. Living with Sebahat was difficult; my every move was closely watched and I felt overpowered. For four years my income had been sent to Turkey to build this new home and I wanted to live in what I had paid for. Mehmet and I went shopping for furniture and no expense was spared. We bought a mahogany dining table for eight with upholstered chairs, and a matching glass and mahogany sideboard, a complete built-in pine bedroom and, as for the living-room, two very large striped sofas and chairs. I decided on a cream and terracotta colour scheme. It was like winning the lottery, out shopping with Mehmet. He had money and a good job and he wanted everyone to know it.

But I became concerned when he chose a bedroom for his mother.

"Please tell me she is not going to live with us?"

"I want my mother by my side."

"Look, we don't get on, you know that. Why in God's name would she want to live with us?"

"Not us, me."

I had a sinking feeling and sat on the balcony with Damla to discuss the situation.

"Jennifer, Sebahat was always going to live with Mehmet. It has been planned for years."

"How the hell can I live with that woman? She hates me!"

"I don't know but you must understand I am happy to lose her. I don't wish you harm but for twenty years I have put up with her. I am only sorry she will be your problem, believe me."

I was feeling like a trapped rat, knowing that I had given all my money for years to help build this damn place and now I would have to live with a woman who hated me! I was nothing but a womb for her son!

The day of the move came. The furniture had been delivered and the rooms were complete. As I was going down the stairs of Dalma's house with my things to the cab, I heard something. I looked up the three flights of stairs and there at the top was Sebahat, covered from head to toe in grey with only her glasses exposed. Slowly she descended, looking straight at my eyes. I knew that she was smiling her sly smile, the one she used with Damla when she cuddled Hakan. As bad as my life with Mehmet was, it was now about to get much worse!

When we arrived at the apartment, Mehmet with his childish smile gave Sebahat the key to open the door to *her* new home! As he said the words I could feel a purge coming on.

I had control over nothing in the apartment. She controlled everything from how the furniture was laid out to what food we would eat. I hated the bitch! If I tried to change anything she told Mehmet.

Just after we moved in, I changed the position of some chairs.

Shortly afterwards, she and Mehmet appeared.

"Why did you upset my mother?"

"All I did was move the chairs – it is my home too, you know!"

"You have nothing, you fucking bitch! This is not your home! You are here as a guest of my mother, and you will do whatever she wants you to do. Get it?"

"Mehmet, I –"

Whack!

I had no time to get the words out. He hit me across the face and she watched him do it!

Life went on like this and I was unable to do a thing about it. I went to work six months after moving to Turkey as a guest relations officer in a hotel. My spoken Turkish was now good enough for me to get out of the house and work. Once more I took refuge in my job. I would work overtime for free, just to stay out of the house, but nothing could change the fact that when I went home she was there.

I had two jailors now.

Mehmet became more demanding and expected me to submit to his mother in every respect. She caused many arguments followed by a beating, followed by rape. It may seem extreme but this was our routine and had been for over four years! We were getting tired of it. We hardly spoke to each other. We both knew any exchange would lead to my being hit. Mehmet told me one evening I was like an untrainable dog!

As he believed that he was part of the 'rich set', we were invited to many evenings out. I had become friends with Anna, another Irishwoman living in Turkey and she definitely belonged to the 'rich set'. Her house alone was amazing – swimming pool/bar/built-in barbecue – it was like a home from the TV. The first day I went round I was shocked. I believed houses like this one were only in America! Cream arched walls throughout the biggest kitchen I have ever been in, outside of a hotel. I could spend hours describing it but just think Hollywood and you're there.

Anna and her husband would invite us to dinner quite a bit. Her husband Tony was a very influential person in the business world and held membership to all the private clubs in town. One evening we went to Club 1739, the home of Fenner Bache, one of the country's biggest football teams. The Who's Who of the football world dined in this club and you could feel it.

Because Mehmet perceived himself to be so important, I had to have the best of clothes. It may sound wonderful but most of the time these expensive clothes were covering my bruised and battered body. I was taken to the important meetings but the rest of the time I was left home with *her*. Mehmet was shagging about town and my only concern was for my health. AIDS was becoming a major world problem at this time and I for one did not want to become infected. I had no idea who he was sleeping with, most likely rich American women. He had plenty of them staying in his hotel

15

About a year after we moved to Turkey, Sebahat decided that Mehmet needed a son. I was called to her room and told this as if I were a waitress taking an order.

"It is time Mehmet had a son. He is not getting any younger and he must have children before it is too late."

Mehmet was ten years older than me and heading for forty at high speed.

"It's not up to you when and if we have children, you know," I said.

"It is my job to look after my son and his interest. I feel it is time for a baby."

"The last time I was pregnant he beat it out of me. We could have a two-year-old now if he had let me be."

You could tell Sebahat was shocked at my revelation but, never one to criticise her beloved son, she just shook her head.

"These things happen. I promise you if you get pregnant again he will not hurt the baby."

"And what about me then?"

"He will not hurt you either." She paused. "You don't practise your religion, do you?"

"Not very often but it's there."

"You need to think about becoming a Muslim if you are going to have a child. It would not be right for the mother and child to be different religions."

"I have no intention of becoming a Muslim. I was brought up a Catholic and that's the way I will stay."

"We will discuss this again later. First you must get pregnant."

I left her room and thought to myself: who the hell does she think she is? But then I realised, if you are treated like a queen all your life, you may come to believe you are one. Her husband had died years earlier when Mehmet was a child. It was now her sons' job to take care of her and she made sure they did.

I never bothered telling Memet about the conversation with his mother and hoped the whole idea would go away.

A few weeks later I was being hit for some reason or another and Sebahat watched.

I went to her room when Mehmet had gone out and asked her: "Why did you not try and help me?"

"My son's marriage is none of my business. It is not my place to interfere."

"You never stop interfering! If we so much as disagree you tell him, knowing he will hit me! Why?"

"Mehmet asked me to tell him everything and I do."

"Even though you know he will hit me?"

"It's what he wants."

"Mehmet is not God and you are not his servant. You

expect me to have a child and live this life forever? Not a chance in hell!"

She began to cry, something she was very good at, so I left her room and went to sit on the balcony.

When Mehmet came home that night and went to her room as usual, I expected to be dragged inside for my beating! But he just went to bed.

The following morning Sebahat went home to her house, saying she missed her friends and wanted to go home for a bit.

One image from Turkey that is with me forever is that of a little boy who used to beg at the top of our road. I used to buy him a kid's meal in Wendy's on my way to work. This little boy broke my heart. He was no more than six yet he sat in the same spot every day from early morning to night. I was aware of how important children were in Turkish culture and was confused by the boy's situation. I discussed him one day with the guy who owned our local shop. Ali told me he was a gypsy child and most likely had his legs broken at birth so he could make a living on the streets. On my way back from work one evening I watched as a BMW pulled up alongside the child. My first thoughts were of abduction and I quickened my pace, thinking of ways to save him. I saw a very well-dressed woman walk towards the boy and he put out his arms calling "Mummy!". Ali had been telling the truth.

I began to think of trying to get Mehmet to adopt a child; little did I know that it would lead to such uproar.

One evening after Sebahat's return, when the three of us were at home and the atmosphere seemed calm, I raised the subject of adoption. Both Sebahat and Mehmet attacked me instantly with words!

"I am only saying that there are children out there being abused like the little boy at the top of our road. We could offer a good home."

Sebahat was furious that I could consider such a thing. "These children are unclean – born out of wedlock or even worse to a Kurdish mother!"

"Surely it would be a good thing to do. Take a child into our home in need of a family?"

Sebahat left the room without answering me. Mehmet followed.

I went to the kitchen to make tea, thinking how selfish they both were. It was a few minutes before I was aware of his presence.

I knew what would happen next.

"Upset my mother, will you? She is in there crying over what you said!"

"All I said is that it would be a good thing to adopt."

"My family do not take in gypsy children! How dare you ask?"

In seconds my tea was on the floor and I was soon to follow.

"You fuckin' Irish whore, how dare you upset my mother! You should wash her feet in thanks for her taking you in!" *Kick!*

I was so taken aback by the washing of her feet bit, I hardly noticed him hitting me. By the time I had digested his words, I noticed his erection and gulped in fear of what was to come next. Mehmet always hurt me when he raped me. I could be sore for days after. A few times I would be raped again before my body had time to recover. I used to wonder sometimes how I had ended up in such an extreme situation where rape and beatings were part of my daily life.

I began spending a lot of time with my friends in the 'rich set'. Mehmet approved of this company and I had some time free from pain. We had some wonderful evenings out. One particular night I went by private yacht on the Bosphorus for dinner and then on to Club 29, a very exclusive club for the rich and famous, to dance the night away. Mehmet was still putting it about and we lived separate lives while he was otherwise occupied.

In Turkey he let me keep my money – after all, what would people think if his wife was penniless and him being such an 'important man'?

At a function one evening I was talking to the Irish consulate and enjoying myself. Mehmet was there, knocking back the whiskey, and came over to our table. He whispered in my ear: "What the fuck do you think you are doing, you whore?"

"I am sitting here talking to this man about Ireland – what did you think I was doing?"

He took my hand under the table and squeezed so tight it felt like he had broken my fingers!

"Mehmet, please, stop! You are hurting me! Please!"

He just squeezed tighter and said in my ear: "You are my wife and I see you smiling at this man. I know what you are doing. You are my wife and don't you forget it."

Mehmet got up and left the table. I sat, trying not to show my pain, then excused myself and went to the loo where I saw my hand swelling and knew he had broken three of my fingers.

I went back and the bastard took me to the dance floor, knowing what he had done. He even insisted on swinging me around by my injured hand. I expected to faint on the spot but somehow made it home.

I knew as soon as I heard the front door close that this was not over! Mehmet had only begun. I shuddered and remained stuck to the spot. How much more pain could he inflict on me this evening?

"So you think you're great, don't you, talking to important men? He could see you are nothing but a no-good whore and he was hoping for a fuck!"

"Don't be so stupid! He was an old man and we were talking about Ireland. Nothing else."

"I saw how he looked at you, hoping for a fuck from you, you whore!"

"Mehmet, please, stop this. We were having a nice night out, then you break my fingers – what more do you want?"

"Want has only started!"

He took me by the hair and dragged me up six flights of stairs. I was crawling on my hands and knees, begging him to stop. His rage ran so deep he needed to hurt as much as possible.

When we got to the flat he refused to allow me to stand up. "Stay on your hands and beg forgiveness, you good-for-nothing!"

In the hallway he threw me by the hair on the floor – this took some force as I was on my hands and knees at the time. Then he kicked me in the stomach and went to bed.

I wrapped my hand and made up a story for the hospital in the morning.

"I fell on the stairs last night."

It was the best I could come up with. The doctor was so nice. He was American and asked what I was doing in Turkey. My scalp was swollen and he looked at it and sighed.

It was not my first visit to this hospital and my name had come up on the computer when he entered it. Mehmet had kicked my back a few weeks before and I had come here for treatment, fearing a disk out of place – thankfully it was only a swelling and my spine had survived the kick.

Now, when the X-rays came back, he looked me in the eye and said: "Jennifer, these injuries could not be caused by a fall. Your fingers are dislocated. What really happened?"

I looked at his knowing eyes, trying to think fast. "Can they be fixed?"

"Yes, thankfully they can be reset and splinted. You didn't answer my question. I see a lot of foreign women. Like you, they fall in love, then move here and are abused. Do you love him?"

"He is all I have. What can I do? My family don't care about me, my mother is dead and I am stuck with Mehmet. I have nowhere to go!"

Whether it is part of this Battered Woman's Syndrome or what, I truly believed that no one wanted me and I was incapable of making it on my own. Maybe it was because Mehmet had told me so many times how useless I was or maybe it was that I felt I had no one to defend me. Whatever the reason I believed I had to stay as there was nothing else for me.

140

"Where did you live before?"

"London. I still have my flat there but it is rented to a Turkish couple."

"You should leave. You were here last month with a back injury. This will only get worse. In all my years I have never seen any of these men change."

"I have a 'run account' but I don't have the strength to go."

"Jennifer, you have to find it before he kills you. I had a woman here last month who will be disfigured for life. She has been here for ten years and we see her at least once a month. Your husband will never change."

I left the hospital and thought about running, but where would I go and who would be there for me? With no self-esteem or confidence, I was sure I could not manage on my own. I felt alone in the world. I knew that somehow I was still a little girl trapped in the past. My need for love and cuddles had never diminished, yet I had a large family. How can this be, I thought.

I went home and purged to relieve my pain.

A few days later the air changed in the house. I don't know who spoke to Mehmet or what happened but he suddenly wanted a child and a caring housewife.

"I want a son. It is time either you give me one or I will find someone else, you hear me?"

"What brought this on? The last time I was pregnant you wanted to kill the baby and now suddenly you want a son. What if we have a girl?"

"Then next time you give me a son."

"I am to be a baby-popper?"

"Look, I gave you a chance when no one wanted you. I even took you to Turkey to live with my friends and family. You have proven to me you can do it and now it is time for a family."

"If I agree, will you stop shagging half of Turkey and be a proper husband? No more beatings. Respect me for who I am. I learned your language, entertained your friends and family. If you want a child, then you must respect me."

"Agreed. And you will convert to Islam."

I hardly heard the last bit as my mind was filling with happy thoughts of a real family. I actually believed the fecker! I was so desperate for love I was about to tie myself to Mehmet forever!

He took me to bed that night and tried to make love to me. He had always been rubbish in bed. It was all about him and lasted only minutes!

In the five years we were together I had never enjoyed sex. It was either angry rape or to satisfy his needs and now it was about a son. I used to wonder if he was as bad in bed with his other women. Mehmet was a good-looking man and a very bad lover. Maybe this is why he used to have different women all the time – once they discovered how bad a lover he was, they probably found someone else.

I often used to think – this man who was as damaged as I was, could he be capable of love? They say that some are born evil. If this is true then Mehmet had all the traits. If we had a son, would he hurt him? What about a daughter? I knew if he did I would run with the child. I started putting money in my 'run account' again, just twenty dollars a week, but I knew it would cost to run with a child. Even with all my doubts I still planned to go ahead with the plan to have a child. I was desperate and in need of love.

Around February '93 I stopped taking the Pill again and hoped that God would bless me with a child to love.

Sebahat came back to our house after another one of her trips to her apartment and tried to be nice to me. The abuse stopped and I was eating healthily. I was now eight stone nine. Mehmet liked me this way and I knew that I must be healthy to have a child. It was almost a surreal existence: the people who hurt me were now taking care of me for a son! Every month I had the same ordeal with Sebahat watching me and asking if I'd had a period. After about four months they all became bored waiting and began to suggest that I might be barren! I had conceived quickly both times before though both times I lost the baby. I am sure nature was just ensuring that my body was ripe for conception this time, but they were impatient and began to show their true colours again.

Sebahat found a half-used packet of the Pill in my room and all hell broke loose. She told Mehmet and watched as he beat me with that sly smile I had become so familiar with on her face.

"You lying whore! You are trying to make a fool out of me! I will kill you, you hear?"

"Mehmet, I am not on the Pill! It is an old pack from last year!"

"Tomorrow I'll have your blood tested and, if you are on the Pill behind my back after promising me a son, I will kill you!"

I was marched, battered and bruised, to the hospital the following morning. Sebahat joined us, eagerly awaiting the results. The American doctor saw me sitting quietly, waiting with the two of them, and smiled a sad smile at me. I felt ashamed and wanted God to take me there and then.

The test proved that I was not lying and a big discussion began with his mother and sister as to why I was not pregnant!

Mehmet was on the late shift that night.

I decided it was time for me to die.

I had a few tablets I found amongst my stuff after we moved to Turkey. I had put them in my coat pocket and they had stayed there for almost two years. Tonight I was going to use them as my way out. I had three morphine slow-release tablets, each ten milligrams, and five thirty-milligram DF118 codeine pills.

I went to the kitchen and made myself tea, then said goodnight to Sebahat. It was about 7 p.m. and Mehmet was on the night shift so I knew he would not be back for a few days, as he slept in the hotel after his shift then went straight on to the next one. He was normally gone for four nights when he was on night shifts.

I knew I would never see Sebahat again and was thankful.

I phoned Daddy to say hi and spoke to Honor for a

few minutes. I said goodbye to both of them and took the pills. I lay and asked God for forgiveness and begged that I be allowed to spend eternity with Mammy. I cried for the lost love I had so wanted in my life. I cried for the babies I would never hold but most of all I cried for the horrible life I had lived and regretted it had been that way. Soon I felt my body give in to the pills and I began to feel warm and comforted. I was about to reach Nirvana, then I was gone.

I opened my eyes twenty-two hours later and cried convulsions when I realised I was alive! Sebahat had been gone all day with her daughter to buy furniture. With her away and Mehmet working it had seemed so perfect – no one would have realised until it was too late and I was gone. Why had God not taken me? Why? I was still here in Turkey alone. I had a headache that almost killed me and found I could not walk around without wanting to puke. I could not believe I had survived but I had to accept it for now. Maybe the pills were out of date? I had taken enough to kill a horse for Christ's sake! Here I was walking around dying with my headache and pissed I was alive.

I would have tried again but I had no more pills.

It then came to me that I had lived for a reason. I remember thinking: 'I am here because I am meant to be here.'

I began to look at myself in the mirror. Even though we had wall-to-wall mirrors in our bedroom, I never looked at myself. 'Dysfunction is unable to look in the mirror for fear of what it will see' – a statement recently made to me by a friend when we discussed eating disorders. I believe it explains how the mind of a person with an eating disorder will almost always see a distorted image of reality.

Now I knew after surviving my suicide attempt that I had a purpose in life and I began to try and accept who I was.

My new resolve as usual lasted only a few days.

I was told a couple of days later that I was going to be blessed by the Imam to help me conceive. I was not working until the evening and went along with them – what harm could it do? I dressed appropriately with my body, face and hair covered, and then took the short walk to the mosque. I really hated that mosque; I was woken at five in the morning with the call to prayer for two years! I wanted at times to shoot the speakers, just to block out the sound. It's not that I had a problem with the call to prayer itself; it was the early alarm-call I hated.

At the mosque, I realised from their discussion that they had told the Imam I wished to convert! Like a trapped rat, once more I had to think fast. I was asked to recite some words from the Koran and knew this in their eyes would convert me.

I did as I was told, all the time saying the 'Our Father' in my head followed by the Creed.

I went later that day to see this Turkish girl I knew. Yasmin and I would meet every now and then. We met through work. She had begun to open up to me and told me her husband through an arranged marriage was hitting her! I was shocked as he had grown up in England and seemed so totally normal.

We understood each other and had the potential to become close friends.

I asked if, in her opinion, what had happened meant I was a Muslim now?

"To become a Muslim you must convert freely – you did not, so nothing has changed."

"They think I have converted."

"But you know you have not. Keep your secret and let them think whatever they want."

"Yasmin, I really needed to hear that, thank you! It's between us?"

"Always."

Mehmet's family were delighted, believing that I had freely converted, while I knew I had not. So strong was their faith, they believed that I would soon deliver the much-sought-after son. I only wished I had the strength to run there and then but I had no one to run to! I was past caring about my family; I was no longer affected by their lack of concern. I was alone as I always had been. This was my life. Long gone was the child in the kitchen with kiss curls. My memory of that, though intact, was less comforting. I would pray to my mother almost daily, asking why? I was so very convinced that I had done something terrible as a child. I carried guilt for no reason. I longed for the soft cuddles under the floppy bit of my mother's arm, like a little chick under the wing of its mother.

Because of my open mind, I now saw my mother for what she was: human. Mam made mistakes; she was not infallible. I loved her anyway. Maybe too much time was spent on other people's problems and I suffered as a result, but she was doing what she thought was right. How could I possibly blame her?

It took another couple of months of turmoil before I conceived. When I told Mehmet the news he was all over me. I was now his wife in every sense of the word. He told me many times during the following few days that he loved me and I believed him.

Sebahat brought her friends to see me with child. I had never really looked too deeply at the culture and was surprised at the fuss that was made of me for the first month. People came with sweets and food for me, I guess as a kind of preparation for pregnancy. Here in the west we all run and take vitamins. It seems in Turkey the women folk take care of you and ensure you eat the right foods. I was enjoying all the attention and hardly noticed that Mehmet was up to his old tricks. Then I realised he was out all night, clubbing again. Before, I used to laugh at a man of his years at the disco – he was thirty-nine and trying rather badly to keep up with the young ones – but I found myself bothered by his behaviour this time.

I made this clear one night when he returned drunk from a club.

"You promised me when I agreed to have your child that we would be a proper couple."

"Fuck you, I don't give a shit! Once I have my son, you can fuck off back to shitty Ireland. Did you honestly believe I was going to let you look after my child?"

"Don't be so stupid! You're drunk!"

"Ask my mother. I will get rid of you once the baby is born and then she will raise it, not you. You fuckin' Irish whore!"

I stepped forward and hit him! I had never done such a thing before, but the thought of him wanting to take my child away made my blood boil over. His mother had come on the scene to see what all the fuss was about and saw what I had done! She was in shock. A wife never hits her husband, never! I was now a shameful woman.

"Hit me, will you? Do that again and I will kill you, baby or no baby! No woman will ever hit me!"

Whack! I laid a smack right in his face.

"You good-for-nothing dirty bitch! Now you will die!"

I couldn't care less. I wanted to die. Mehmet came at me with such force I was knocked straight on the ground and he punched and kicked with all his strength as I waited for death to come. Sebahat stopped him, screaming that he would go to prison and what about the child! He left me there on the floor and went to bed, as did Sebahat without asking if I was all right.

It was then I realised that they would take my child from me and I planned my escape.

I went to see the American doctor the following morning to make sure my child was OK and I was safe to fly. I told him my plan and he made a phone call to book me on a British Airways flight to London that night. Mehmet was on the night shift again and I knew I could get out. He hugged me and wished me a good life as I promised never to return.

I went back to the flat and put my money and our joint credit card in my pocket. I also found my passport, which I had concealed among my knickers.

The next five hours were hell. Mehmet went to work at five and still showed no concern for me or his child. Sebahat ignored me all day and this suited me fine. If I behaved nervously they must have put it down to the night before.

At around six o'clock Sebahat was downstairs with her daughter, who also lived in the building. I went down to say I was invited to dinner with a Turkish friend of mine. I had asked her to cover for me, telling her I wanted to see my Irish friend. This Turkish woman too had an unhappy marriage so we had solidarity between us. I had covered for her a few times. She was a well-educated Turkish woman and had an arranged marriage with a man of similar social stature – he too was a wife-beater and controlled her every move. Mehmet and himself were friends and although I hardly knew the girl I would cover for her when she wanted to go out with her friends by saying we would be meeting up for dinner – this was acceptable to both men. I knew I could trust her and she agreed.

It was going to be impossible for me to take any of my things with me, only the clothes I stood in. I could not get caught. I had to make it out of the country; then I could make plans. Go into a shelter, do whatever I had to do to save my child from this madman.

I walked up town to get a taxi, so as to make sure not to leave a trail behind me. The taxis on our street were regulars and they would tell or question why I was going to the airport with no luggage. I couldn't risk it.

Once at the airport I checked in. When they asked about luggage I said I had received a phone call – my mother was dying and I had to come straight here to get home with no time to pack. The girl at the British Airways desk accepted my explanation and gave me a sad smile, thinking I was rushing to Ireland to be at the side of my dying mother.

I phoned my old school friend Anita in Camden, telling her I would be coming to her flat but giving no details. She had been coming and going from Ireland over the years and, luckily for me, had now settled in London. We had met occasionally and in secret as Mehmet did not want me associating with Irish people. But when we were together it was as if we had never been apart.

I had two hours to take off. My heart pounded and I was sure Mehmet would walk through the door and catch me. If he did I knew I would die! The minutes passed so slowly I was a wreck when it came to boarding. There were very few passengers that night and I sat at the back of the plane as I had requested at check-in and prayed that I would get away safely.

Eventually the doors closed and the plane prepared for take-off. We had to wait and I was sure that Mehmet had got the police to stop the plane. My mind was going through every conceivable possibility! I was sure he would board the plane any minute.

As we roared down the runway the tears fell as I let go of my pent-up emotion. I cried for my freedom and thanked God for giving me this chance. I am sure I even promised to go to Mass!

The steward noticed me crying and thought I was

afraid of flying. He sat with me and I blurted out the whole story. He got up and went to get some champagne. "We will celebrate your freedom in style!" he said. The plane was so quiet that he stayed with me the whole time, surreptitiously drinking and celebrating. All four of the economy staff joined me for a secret drink during the last hour of the flight. They had flown a virtually empty plane and no one could see them down the back with me – the senior hostess was in first class. I told them my story and as that BA flight flew at forty-two thousand feet that night, we made merry as it took me home.

16

I arrived at Anita's flat in Camden at around seven on the Friday morning. I was walking on air and carrying the two mini-bottles of champagne the flight crew had given me for us to celebrate.

I had no idea what was happening back in Turkey but, when I phoned my tenants to give them notice to quit, they told me that they had been bombarded with calls from Mehmet. They were going to Turkey for a couple of weeks on the Monday so they had no objection if I wanted to stay in the flat. We had been friends before I went to Istanbul, now they were offering me assistance in my time of great need. I hated Mehmet now and hoped he was suffering. I told my tenants if he called again just to say I had a breakdown and was staying in the flat for a couple of weeks when they went away, to get well. I knew he would fall for that and calm down, believing I would go back in a few weeks. He would relax, knowing I was in the flat. He would never believe that I would leave him for good, let alone make it on my own. After all, I had always gone back in the past. Jennifer would never be strong enough to disobey him! He was in for a shock this time.

I went to St Thomas' early-pregnancy unit that day. When the nurses saw my bruises and heard my story, they booked me in for the scan immediately. I saw on the screen my beautiful little baby moving around full of life. I was so happy and went on a shopping spree with Mehmet's credit card. I spent seven hundred and fifty pounds on clothes – everything from underwear to shoes.

I spent the weekend with my friend Anita, unsure of what I was going to do with my future. We talked and made plans.

I moved back to my flat on the Monday. I felt I was imposing on Anita – she had a child to look after and did not need me too. I was welcome to stay as long as I liked but felt that it was better to start my new life. After all, it was my flat, I loved it and I was going to make it my home. The day I put the key in the door I felt so proud I had a home and best of all it was only in my name. I would use the law to protect myself if need be. I knew I had some time before the trouble started. I had, after all, run to Ireland in the past and returned to Mehmet. It was so lucky my tenants were going back to Turkey for a holiday at the same time as I needed a place to stay. It was fate.

I began looking for a job but on Monday afternoon something bugged me about the baby. I knew that all was not well and went to the early-pregnancy unit once more. I begged for another scan. They thought I was a madwoman. I had been told that everything was fine only two days before! I begged and pleaded, then reluctantly they agreed to scan me at the end of the day.

I waited for hours until I was called, then there in the darkened room on the screen was my baby – dead! I panicked as the doctor explained that I had to be booked in the following day to deliver! I told the doctor in no uncertain terms that they had made a mistake, that the machine was not working and my child was alive and well and not to bother with an appointment for me. I went home and cried for hours.

Then I made some calls, to my father and Sebahat – I wanted her to know that the baby she so wanted was dead.

She was distraught and was screaming, "How could the baby die?"

I screamed back: "Your bloody son beat me four days ago, that's why!"

He phoned me late that night and told me he knew I'd had an abortion and he hoped I rotted in hell! I know he told his family this also – the coward was afraid to face the truth.

I went to bed that night and cried out in pain for hours. Suddenly a calm came over me. It was probably exhaustion but I felt so peaceful and calm I slept.

Since I was very young I had always hoped to have a little girl and call her Shauna – I had first heard the name in school and it stuck with me. Now I dreamed my daughter Shauna had given her soul for mine. I was a bit of a Buddhist and believed in reincarnation. I still do. Shauna had come to free me. I carried this child for such a short time and now she was taken away! Yet I knew it was the right thing. My little angel had saved me. It was this belief that kept me going throughout the ordeal.

I turned up the following morning in the unit. The doctor had booked me in and I knew straight away that he had experience of this type of denial before; he somehow knew that I would come to my senses. I was told later that I had been carrying a girl. I needed desperately to know the sex of my baby so that I could attribute a name. Of course, I knew her name: Shauna.

The hospital insisted I had to be brought home by someone on the Tuesday night or stay in! I could not be discharged alone; I must have someone to stay with me that night. My tenants were in Turkey; still I told the doctor that they would be in the flat with me overnight. All I needed was someone to come and pick me up. I racked my brains. Here I was, alone as usual, with no one to help me. I didn't want to ask Anita as she was busy with her own baby, so I kept thinking, until I thought of Yusuf, Mehmet's ex-boss, the owner of the Turkish restaurant. He had a driver and had always had a soft spot for me. I phoned Yusuf and he came to my rescue. He sent one of the waiters I knew to take me home.

I went to bed that night and prayed to Shauna. I believed in my dream and still do. I was so grateful to her for saving me. My beautiful little angel was my saving grace and would always be with me, of this I was sure. I will never forget her sacrifice, ever.

I woke the following morning and knew I could not be alone. I knew deep inside that I was sick with grief and desperately in need of company. I decided to phone Dolores in Spain where she had moved a few years before. We both agreed that it would be better if I went and stayed with her for a few weeks until I was strong enough to move forward.

Dolores had lost a child in almost identical circumstances. Her baby just died, as did Shauna, with neither rhyme nor reason to the death. "She just died" – "It just happened" – a doctor's favourite lines and something I had to accept in order to recover. I kept my angel thoughts as a way of making sense of the tragic event; it helped lessen the pain.

I put the joint credit card to good use once more and made my way to Malaga. I had no sooner unpacked when Dolores' husband Douglas received a phone call that his Aunt Barbara was dying back in Galway. Barbara had MS and had been in a nursing home for years.

I remember thinking that I too had MS. I have no idea where the thought came from and this was the second time it had. The first time, on the escalator in Victoria station, I saw a big poster about the disease and remember thinking, 'I have that', but I put it to the back of my mind.

Douglas made his way to Galway and I stayed with Dolores and little Doug, hoping that I would not have to go home. I needed company but not in Galway. I knew if I were to survive I would have to stay in London. I would be overpowered at home and I needed to become 'Jennifer' once more, something I had to do alone. I knew that I would never recover in the family. I had to be alone. I had to find the strength inside me to become the person I should have been all along.

Within a few days, the call I dreaded came and we packed up to go home for the funeral. If only Barbara had lasted a couple of weeks more, I could have avoided this trip. I swore Dolores to secrecy; so far Anita and Dolores were the only people who knew I had left Mehmet! And I wanted it to stay that way.

Back home everyone was busy with Christmas and I managed to slope into the background. The questions were few; it seemed they were all avoiding the subject of my miscarriage. Not once did anyone ask how I was feeling or say they were sorry for my loss. It was like she did not exist, so I told them nothing. Shauna was my daughter and if her death was so unimportant then I would not discuss it.

It was years later before I had the discussion with my sisters. They had no idea how far along my pregnancy had been – I was four months – let alone the fact that I knew the sex. We'd had very little contact with each other while I lived in Turkey. I only ever phoned Dad and I received virtually no phone calls!

I was always going to be on the outskirts of my family. We were different people and had little if anything in common. I lacked nurture and felt little attachment yet I never stopped trying to be accepted. I was always the one who worried about the others. From when I was a little girl I used to worry if my sisters were late home – we shared a bedroom and I often woke and saw their beds empty. I would lie there awake, worried that something had happened, until I heard the familiar sounds of their voices.

Now I wanted so badly for them to come and care for me. I know I would run back to London every time and that they tried to get me to leave Mehmet but I wanted them to accept him and just come to visit me when I was in hospital or experiencing some problem or another. I guess I wanted it all. The emotions of the little girl still crying out for comfort.

The time had come for me to be strong. I had to take control of my life and ensure I was never hurt again. This rose was about to bud though I knew it would take time to blossom.

I managed to survive the holiday, spending most of my time with Andy and his wife Mary. I even managed to laugh a few times. My priority now was to stay strong.

17

I went back to Tulse Hill and soon found work in a hotel. I had been surviving on my 'run money', which was quickly diminishing.

Some time later I went to a solicitor and began divorce proceedings. I told him everything but decided I had to be careful what I put in the decree for fear Mehmet would refuse to sign the papers. I was being harassed by telephone. He was so out of control. One night he told me he was across the road and was coming to kill me! In his sadistic manner, he described how I was going to die a slow death at his feet. I phoned Brixton police station in panic. When the policewoman arrived, she decided to phone the house in Turkey just to see if Mehmet had actually travelled to the UK. He answered. She was very pissed off with him and told me to change my number. The incident was logged in case of further problems.

Mehmet did arrive in London some time later. I told him when he phoned I had a barring order and if he as much as knocked on my door he would be arrested. He stayed away but begged me to meet him so we could discuss our future.

I had been in counselling a few months. Women's Aid were true to their word and helped me remain strong. Violence is something most women would run from at the first sign but then there are the ones like me, so battered and bruised both physically and emotionally that it is easier to go back to the abuser than it is to begin again.

My therapist was a guy called Tony. We met as often as possible. It was his words that over time and through memory helped me believe in me.

"Jennifer, you are a wonderful human being and have so much to offer. You *will* one day find happiness."

"I can't ever see myself trusting again. I don't hate men, I fear them. Every night I wake up sweating and crying in fear of the future and the past. Mehmet has managed to convince me that I am not good enough to exist and those around me do little to make me feel I am worth saving."

"This is about you and you only. No one else matters. I can honestly say you have a lot to offer this world."

Tony's words kept me fighting. I even had the courage to attend a meeting for people with eating disorders. The group were called Overeaters Anonymous! I walked into the hall to find the place full of anorexics. Somehow the name didn't quite fit the group. Hosting support groups for people with eating disorders was a pretty new concept in the early '90's. I knew if I were to try and stop purging alone, I would fail, and the weekly group meetings helped

JENNIFER BANKS

me accept I had a problem. But I would need one on one if I were to try and recover fully.

Once I told my solicitor that Mehmet was in the country, he jumped at the chance of serving the papers. It would not matter if Mehmet refused to sign for the divorce. All that was important was that the papers were served. With my new-found confidence I arranged to meet him in the burger bar in Streatham near my solicitor's office. I would hand him the envelope and my solicitor would stand at the bus stop outside where he would have a full view of the papers being handed over.

Mehmet was charming, so much so it reminded me of when we first met. I had to be strong and handed over the papers, ensuring first that the solicitor was watching. I sat and had a cup of tea with Mehmet. He tried to take my hand, stroke my face, anything to try and draw me back in. I told him I had moved on from the life we lived and needed peace. If he cared for me at all, then he would leave me alone. It was the least I deserved.

Mehmet seemed actually saddened to realise I did not love him. I had realised that I never had. I could see the hurt in his eyes.

I was almost beginning to believe we might have a chance when he said: "You look well but have gained a few pounds! Surely you're not letting my years of hard work making you thin go to waste?"

"How dare you! You have no right to speak to me like that! I am free from your hurt now. I am no longer your wife and my weight has nothing to do with you!"

162

He lowered his voice. "Until these fuckin' papers are through, you are still my wife and don't you forget it!"

"What the hell are you talking about?"

"You will not see men or have sex. If you do and I hear, then I will kill you."

"Don't you dare make threats! I can do what I bloody well like! You are nothing more to do with me!"

"You think so, do you? In my law you are not free until I say so. If you bring my name down you will die. I know people in this country and they will do it for me so be very careful what you do, you hear?"

"This is England. You can't touch me here so don't bother with your threats! I will live my life as I choose – get it?"

I gathered my things. Mehmet had brought me my jewellery box with the few possessions I had inside but told me if I wanted my photographs then I had to go to Turkey to get them.

As I was leaving he made his final threat and I could tell by his eyes he meant what he was saying.

"Remember I know people and for a thousand pounds I can have your throat cut. My friends will be watching you so be very very careful!"

My solicitor had returned to his office across the street once he had seen the exchange and I got a taxi back to my flat, locked the door and purged.

I began to have one-on-one counselling. I had to find out why I was this way, bulimic and worthless. This was how I felt and had been feeling for sixteen years. How had this happened? My only hope of recovery was to answer the hard questions.

I had never felt important or loved. My early years were fine but once I started school it was like I disappeared off the family radar. I had the material goods but I lacked the acknowledgement of my existence. I was funny and appeared to be full of life to the people outside of my secret world; in truth I was hurting badly.

Facing reality was difficult and my bulimia was exacerbated to the point where my throat was constantly burning from the bile I purged, once I had emptied the contents of my often empty stomach.

In one particular session my counsellor Elizabeth insisted I faced a few facts.

"The past is irreversible. You must heal the wounds yourself."

"How the hell can I?"

"You must learn to forgive the hurt."

"It's not possible. Do you know how many nights I lie in bed crying in pain, trying to understand why the hell my family don't care? Why I was left in hospital, not knowing if I would die? And still no one came. Have you any idea how it feels to be so unimportant that people don't care if you die?"

I had to run and purge! My body had become accustomed to purging if I was in pain or fearful, so much so it was an automatic reflex!

Like the AA twelve-step programme to recovery, I too had to take steps to learn to love myself first in order to heal. I had endured pain and hurt for so many years it would be another few before I was even on the doorstep of recovery. I was trying and that was all I could do for now. I had a job, my flat and Mehmet seemed to be leaving me alone to get on with it.

I went to Ireland at the beginning of June '94, and it was then I informed the family that I had long ago left Mehmet. I was surprised by the lack of reaction after all the screaming matches in the past trying to get me to leave him and come back home. Now that I had actually left him and was living in London for the past seven months seemed unimportant to the very people who had begged me to leave him for so many years. I wanted to scream at everyone: "I am free! Mehmet is out of my life! I am even trying to work out why you all left me on my own when I needed you most!" I kept it to myself as usual.

Part of recovery is coming to terms with what has happened and trying to make sense of the situation. Elizabeth was determined to help me face the demons. I had been seeing her since February and we were in April now and I still avoided the difficult questions

"What, in your mind, attracted you to Mehmet?"

"The short answer is that he was nice to me."

"Surely telling you to lose weight in order to be with him is not being nice? There had to be more."

"Mehmet was interested in my wellbeing or so he told me. I believed he cared and wanted the best for me. I was unhappy with my body and he agreed with me – then he tried to help me lose the weight. If my self-esteem was higher I would have shut the door on him but I had spent ten years hating myself when Mehmet came along. I guess the attraction was him actually showing an interest in me."

Elizabeth started giving a long talk about the unloved seeking abusers unintentionally, because they appear to care! Sometimes I found therapy so boring. I needed the help to gain strength for my future and the self-esteem in order to survive but I had become so impatient that I now wanted an instant recovery.

I gave up on the weekly sessions.

With the help of meditation and visualisation I began to help myself.

I soon realised that I had allowed the abuse because I had little love for myself and began building up my esteem by concentrating on the good things around me.

I loved my job and began to socialise with my co-workers. Going to the wine bar after work and having a laugh was what I had missed out on for years. Laughter was minimal in my previous life and I was determined to make it a central part of my recovery. I would often go to the comedy club or Brixton Academy where so many of the up-and-coming comedians put on shows to try out their acts before going to Edinburgh. I loved to laugh the night away. I would go home feeling whole and light-hearted. I was also gaining strength in personality. No one was ever going to hurt me again.

However, throughout my self-therapy, the bulimia was active on a daily basis. I would come home from a night out and purge, not knowing why I was doing it. I was as always alone.

I am not a vengeful person and never have been but I

wanted in some way to hurt Mehmet after all he had done to me. I needed revenge, but how? It is difficult to try and find peace when you have been through such a traumatic situation. The mind begs vengeance yet the soul cowers. I would have momentary lapses throughout the day where I would dream of Mehmet paying the price for my suffering. One of my most regular daydreams would have my brothers hunt him down and beat him as he beat me. This in many ways gave me a feeling of belonging: my own brothers were so angry at the way I had been treated that they sought revenge in my honour. I felt important thinking that my brothers cared so much about me that they were willing to do such a thing – I shook off the daydream and entered reality with an empty heart. I still craved acceptance from my family!

I received a call out of the blue one night from Yusuf! I had a feeling Mehmet put him up to it, his way of making sure I knew he was still around. Mehmet had gone back to Turkey after a month and I had become comfortable knowing he was not going to appear in front of me at any moment. I went out for champagne and ice cream with Yusuf. The guy was a multi-millionaire so we had the best champagne available. Yusuf admitted Mehmet had asked him to check up on me. They had met in Yusuf's Istanbul restaurant the week before. We talked and drank for hours, so much so that when he took me back to his apartment to arrange a car to take me back home, I was totally plastered.

I don't know exactly what happened next but somehow I was in bed with this guy! Mehmet's words were ringing in my ears: "I know people who will kill you for a thousand pounds!" Christ, I had to get out of there!

I left as soon as I was dressed, making sure Yusuf was aware of the fact that I was not a tart.

"Yusuf, I have no idea how that happened. I am not a tart and I don't sleep around."

"It was meant to happen, Jennifer. Don't worry. I will tell no one. It is our secret."

When I got home I suddenly thought: "To hell with Mehmet!" If he knew what I had just done with the man he was so jealous of, it would twist his gut. I had just been handed the most wonderful revenge. I was still married to Mehmet and I had just slept with his friend! I felt elated – I was free. The downside was it was the worst sex I have ever had in my life! The guy was a worse lover than Mehmet! He kept repeating "You are beautiful!" over and over again! I was so bloody bored I just wanted it over. I found myself thinking of what to wear to work, while he went through what I guess was his usual routine.

18

I received a letter from my solicitor on the 22nd of June '94 saying that even though Mehmet had not returned his papers, my divorce had been granted application to the courts. At first I thought I was divorced until I realised the proceeding had only just begun. This was leave to celebrate.

I phoned Anita and we arranged to go out on the Saturday for lunch. We went up to Camden Town and spent the day in a very cool hippy restaurant drinking unmeasured glasses of wine – there were no wineglasses in this place and you were getting at least double the usual measure. We were having a ball! I felt totally free with Anita, something I had been unable to feel all my life. I knew I was a nice person and I knew that my friends liked me. The old insecurities of the past were suppressed and hidden away.

The 23rd of June was to be the day that changed my life through the most amazing twist of fate. It was also the third anniversary of my mother's death. I have always felt that she played a part in the twist. I got back to the flat and a programme was about to begin on the radio, called *Midnight Encounters*. It was a dating programme where you phoned in and were interviewed on air. Those interested in you wrote to the station and the letters were vetted and forwarded on. It was all very safe. High on wine and full of devilment, I phoned in. Later I had no idea what I'd said – something about my blonde curls – and I giggled like a child – I could remember laughing down the phone. The following morning I was a little embarrassed but passed the episode off as a bit of fun.

A few weeks later the letters arrived! What Anita and I called a 'Lambrusco Night' was required to read them. I had no intention of replying to any of them – it was, after all, just a bit of fun.

The letters from the radio station were disposed of. I did however keep one. Something about the way it had been written made me keep it. I told a few people about the letter and after weeks of uncertainty I replied, giving only my phone number.

Steve Banks had given his brother's address as he didn't live in London. The station, LBC, was available only to London listeners and he was up from Devon for the weekend to paint his sister's bathroom when he heard me on the radio. I believe it was this that intrigued me: he had never listened to LBC before and stopped the dial when he heard my voice on the airways. He could, of course, be lying and I was not prepared to take a chance. It was for this reason I gave only my first name and telephone number.

I was very busy for the next few weeks with work and

my divorce proceedings. I seemed to have to produce letter after letter to get the thing moving and as for work it was the height of summer in London and the tourists were flooding the place. Hotel reception is the frontline and at times the girls and I used to almost die on our feet working back-to-back shifts. After a particular busy day I was relaxing at home listening to music when the phone rang. I debated answering it but fear that my father might be unwell made me pick up.

Steve was on the other end and we slipped easily into conversation about our day's work. He was on contract work in Peterborough when he called me. We spoke for about an hour and I enjoyed his friendly voice and relaxed nature. We hung up with him promising to call again. To be honest I didn't expect him to. After all, I was sure we were both just passing time. A few days later Steve called again and we went on like this for weeks until one day I picked up, expecting it to be him, and it was Mehmet.

He was back in London and wanted to save our marriage! He loved me and was willing to fight for it! I had my number changed within hours. I was never so fearful in my life. What if he had found out about my drunken night with Yusuf and had returned to kill me? I phoned Brixton police to make them aware of the situation and my solicitor was working on papers to file a harassment charge if he tried to contact me again.

I tried calling Steve at his sister's house to give him my new number but there was never anybody there. I tried almost every day at different times and I was just about to give up when someone answered. In fact, Steve's sister had moved out of her house as she was managing a pub for the summer months as a live-in landlady. The night I had decided to make what was going to be my final phone call, Steve just happened to be in the house with his brother-in-law to pick up his golf clubs. Another twist of fate!

I told him what had happened and we decided to meet up the following Friday night. I still only knew this guy over the phone and to play safe I met him in the George Canning pub in Brixton where I had someone I knew keep an eye out just in case.

Steve and I had no idea what the other looked like. He had told me he looked like a boxer. To be honest, I was unsure of meeting him after he said this. I imagined a big muscular man with tattoos, the lot. Everything I hated.

On my way to the pub I spotted this guy in a phone box. We both looked at each other with a knowing glance and as soon as he arrived at the pub we laughed about the moments before and wondered how we knew each other straightaway without ever having met before.

He was no boxer look-alike – that had been a joke. Steve was a normal man about 5ft 8 and slightly stocky and thankfully no tattoos or piercings! We talked all evening and there was an easy comfort about us. It was as if I had known him all my life. From then on we became friends, chatting on the phone and, as Steve had moved to London with his job as a decorator, we would meet whenever possible.

I was about to begin a new job in Butlers Wharf on the South Bank in a restaurant, Cantina Del Ponte, near Tower Bridge. What worried me was that as long as I was in the hotel trade Mehmet could find me.

A few weeks later he arrived at my flat without warning. I refused to open the door and told him he was in breach of my barring order (I'd never actually got round to getting one). I said I would phone the police if he did not go and he would be arrested. I managed to get rid of him by agreeing to meet him in town for a chat a few days later.

The following evening I received a phone call from him. He was drunk and across the road in a call-box. This time I knew he was really there. How he got hold of my telephone number I will never know, but he did, and now I was at his mercy. He could call and scare me whenever he felt like it.

I called Steve after Mehmet's phone call. I was hiding behind the TV unit in fear for my life; I was sure he knew about Yusuf and had come back to London to kill me in retaliation. Poor Steve was almost thirty miles away and wanted to drive to my rescue. I refused, believing that Mehmet would kill him if he saw him there. I really liked Steve and I knew the feeling was mutual. So far we were just friends but I had a feeling we were destined for more. I also knew it would be too dangerous for us to see each other with Mehmet in town. I would have to make a decision but how?

I met Mehmet as planned and tried to make him understand I did not love him and never had. We went to McDonald's in Leicester Square. I felt so brave I even ate a meal in front of him, hoping he would understand I was no longer afraid and it was over. Inside I was fearful; being in Mehmet's company brought all the memories flooding back. This man had almost killed me and had murdered two of my unborn babies, yet here he was trying to win me back!

"If you come back to Turkey with me, everything will be different, I promise."

"Mehmet, you and I both know that as soon as you lose your temper you will hit me again."

"I love you, Jennifer, and I swear I will never again hit you."

"How many times have you promised to take care of me? As soon as you get stressed, bored or angry I become your punch-bag. No more, Mehmet. This is my life now and no one is going to hurt me again."

"It was your fault that I hit you! If you had behaved and done as you were told then I would have no reason to fight with you. Everything is different now you're not fat and my friends and family like you!"

"So I'm a trophy? You only want to be with me because your friends like me? No way, Mehmet. It is over and I will never go back to you. Please leave me to get on with my life and you yours."

"You will regret this. No one will ever care for you the way I did! You will always be a stupid Irish bitch – you will never be happy ever!"

"Believe what you want. You never cared for me. You hurt me, broke me and degraded me! Now I want to live my own life without you. I don't love you, Mehmet. I never did. You held me through control and I have managed to break free. I will never go back."

"Have it your way, you fuckin' fool! You will come begging me to take you back when you realise that nobody wants you and then I will say 'You had your chance. Now fuck off!'. This will happen!"

I left Mehmet sitting in McDonald's and made my way to Butlers Wharf for work. I kept looking behind as I crossed the bridge, believing he was following and would throw me into the river! Even when I arrived at the restaurant I was unnerved. I felt that I would never be safe again. Even now Mehmet had some control!

I had promised to telephone Steve after I met Mehmet to let him know how I got on. I arrived at work and asked to use the telephone. The restaurant manager was a right cow and refused, so I took my things and left. I used the call-box outside, then went home. I had a fair bit of money in my account and could afford to walk out on my job. I had dealt with enough stuck-up bitches in my life and today this one was one too far. I was better than that. No twenty-year-old child was going to tell me what I could and couldn't do. It was a simple phone call and the place was empty at the time, so what was her problem? I couldn't care less. I upped and left.

Steve was still at work so I left a message with his sister. I was only home when the phone rang. Steve was coming up to Tulse Hill and we would go out for a coffee. We went in to Trafalgar Square and walked around for hours. I had lived in London for eight years but had never taken the time to look at the monuments until now. Steve and I were like kindred sprits – we could be silent together without feeling uncomfortable. I really felt I had found a friend for life. We drove home listening to the radio and chatting easily about nothing and everything. Steve came in for a few minutes, as he had to get back to Hampton Court for work the following morning. He was with a new painting contractor and they had a rush job on. We said goodbye and he got into the car.

As soon as he turned the key, the car died in a cloud of smoke!

"Steve, get out of the car quick in case it blows!"

"Don't worry – it's just my fan belt. The darn thing has snapped. I'll have to call the AA."

"Come on in. I'll put the kettle on."

Steve's AA cover was not 'priority' so we settled down to wait. As it happened, Steve stayed the night. We talked until the early hours. I told him everything about my life with Mehmet – I hadn't hidden the fact I had been married before – I even said so on the radio that fateful night. It was the painful details I had omitted until now. I never mentioned my eating disorder. I just said Mehmet starved me and I became ill from lack of food. Steve didn't question me further.

Eventually I went to bed around six, leaving Steve to sleep on the sofa. Most men would have made a move on me that night but not Steve. We both knew deep down that our relationship was heading towards something more than friendship. The timing was not right that night and we both knew it.

Only a week later at Hampton Court Fair, Steve won me a giant toy rabbit and I know it was at that exact moment I fell in love. For the first time in my life I felt real love and it was overpowering and wonderful at the same time.

We made love that night. I had never felt so loved before. Steve made me feel beautiful and appreciated and I loved him back. I never knew sex could feel so good; my only experiences were either painful or uncaring. Everything felt so natural with Steve. It was as if we were both born for this moment. I was damaged goods and Steve had also been hurt in his previous relationship – about the same time I left Mehmet, Steve and his long-term girlfriend also broke up – but somehow that night we were both healed.

I did get a hell of a shock when I saw he was circumcised! We had not mentioned religion. Did I just fall in love with another Muslim? Of course, he could be Jewish. I had to ask before this went any further. I could not go back after so long moving forward.

It was with trepidation I asked the burning question: "Steve, how come you're circumcised?"

"I have no idea. Why do you want to know?"

"You're not Muslim, are you?"

"No! Actually I don't have any religion, never did. My dad doesn't believe in organised religion, so I must be an atheist!"

"Thank God!"

"Now if that's not a pun, I don't know what is. You don't have to worry about me, Jen. I don't want to control you or anyone else for that matter."

"You know this won't be easy. I have a lot of baggage."

"Who doesn't these days? Look, don't worry about it. We can get through this."

"As long as you understand I could have issues along the way. I am not even fully divorced yet."

"Ah, so I'm having an affair with a married woman?"

"It looks that way."

"Great, I always wondered what that would be like."

Later I made sausage sandwiches and we sat in the bed eating our sandwiches and chatting. My God, this all felt so natural! Could it really be happening? I would ask myself that question many times over the next few months.

I began temping again – I was not the sort to sit at home

watching the TV. I heard nothing from Mehmet. I knew he was still in London but he appeared to be leaving me alone. I was so happy and walked on air for the next few weeks. Steve had his car fixed and would stay over with me every weekend. His job was on the outskirts of London, some twenty-five miles from my house, and it made no sense for him to travel that distance every day.

Our conversations turned to meeting the parents one evening.

"I want to take you to Cornwall to meet my parents, Jen. I've told my father and mother about you and feel it's time for them to meet you."

"Jesus, Steve, what if they hate me? I have already dealt with the mother-in-law from hell and can't go through it again!"

"It's not like before. We're going for the weekend, not to live with them! Don't worry about it. I'm sure they'll like you and if not, tough. I love you and that's all that counts."

"OK, what about next Friday night after work?"

I had no idea about distance in the UK and imagined that it would take a couple of hours to get from London to Cornwall. How wrong can you be!

We left that Friday about seven o'clock. The journey took six hours with a few romantic stop-offs along the way – one in particular in a place called Tregeland holds fond memories.

June and Ernest had waited up to meet me. I can't tell you how relieved I was to see two ordinary people standing before me. No veils or sly smiles, just genuine interest in the girl Steve had brought to meet them. I got on particularly well with Ernest – we were both interested in all things unusual and talked for hours on end about politics and religion – all the world's problems were solved in an evening when Ern and I got together. I used to say to him: "What we need is a country to run!"

June was more interested in Steve and at first I thought this was reminiscent of the past! But Steve was not Mehmet and June was not Sebahat. This was a normal mother-son relationship – and I thanked God.

Now that I had met the Banks family, it seemed a natural progression for Steve to meet the McGraths. I was a wreck taking him home for fear it would not go well but our week in Ireland went without a hitch. My dad loved Steve and my brother Andy struck up a friendship with him. Steve was in awe of Irish life and loved my family – I began to think I had imagined the past! I soon realised that happiness allows you to see things in a different light. I found my family's company a delight and I was spoken to, not at. This would go on until years later when the old problems of the past would once more appear.

19

Back in London, Steve and I settled into our new life together. I had never expected to be in another relationship, let alone so soon after my torturous experience with Mehmet. Steve listened when I talked and held me when I woke up from the nightmares – he was unfazed by my past and wanted only to help me heal. I was experiencing real love for the first time in my life – I was happy and content.

So why did I have to purge every day? I was so sure that being happy would cure my eating disorder but in fact it intensified it. I was so fearful of gaining weight – what if Steve turned off me? I was convinced if I put weight on, it would destroy what I now had!

Steve still had no idea about my bulimia. It was still my secret. I desperately wanted it to go away and tried so hard to stop but I was addicted to the purging. I needed the feeling to get through the day. I had begun purging at work to keep the secret hidden from Steve. My flat was small and, unlike Mehmet, who enjoyed hearing me purge my food, knowing it hurt me, I knew that Steve would be concerned if he heard me in the toilet forcing my body to throw up. It is not something that can be done quietly on an empty stomach. So I carried on in secret and alone.

Mehmet suddenly appeared again out of the blue. He phoned saying a friend I knew in Turkey was in London on holidays and wanted to meet me. I could not have this man in my life any more and cried after his phone call – here he was trying to destroy the happiness I had found and I was at a loss as to how to stop him. I was still married to Mehmet and I knew if he found out about Steve he would have me killed.

Steve and I sat for hours and talked about what to do.

"We can't stay here, Jen. You're terrified of the bastard. Why not move to Devon with me, away from Mehmet and all the Turkish people you are convinced he has watching you?"

"This is my home, my flat – how can I just leave it all behind? I love this place, my job, everything about London! This is home."

"And what if he comes knocking and I'm not here? Do you really want to live in fear of the bastard for the rest of your life? If you really want to stay then we will, but I know you will never be free here."

"I love you, Steve, and want us to stay together – my divorce is almost through – then Mehmet can't touch me ever again."

"Do you honestly think a piece of paper will stop a man who has abused you for seven years?"

We went on like this all night until we decided the

move was the only way for me to escape the threat of Mehmet.

I had left it all behind in Turkey and Ireland but that was easy – neither felt like home. Leaving London was going to be the hardest thing I had ever done – this was my home.

Once the decision was made I wanted to leave straight-away. The only problem was he had to give a month's notice to his tenant in Devon where he owned a house and, I was so afraid for my life, a month was too long. So we decided we would stay with his parents until his house was free.

A master plan was devised. I arranged to meet Mehmet in town one Saturday morning and that morning Steve and I loaded up a van with all my worldly goods and headed off to Cornwall. It would mean that we would be out of work for the duration but I had plenty of money saved and was unconcerned about it.

The Friday before leaving London I had received a call from my employment agency – an old English bank wanted me to work for them. The position was Customer Relations – the pay was £25,000 a year including clothing allowance! I was crushed. I knew that in Devon pay was not good. I was used to earning money now – over the past year I had been able to hold on to my wages with no Mehmet to take it away. How would I survive in Devon? But once the initial shock wore off I knew I had to run – if I wanted a life with Steve. Staying would destroy us. I had no option but to start again.

While Mehmet waited in Leicester Square for me to turn up, I was loading the van. We hit the road at exactly eleven o'clock, the time I had arranged my meeting with Mehmet.

I cried in the bathroom that first night in Cornwall – had I made the right decision? I had made so many bad ones in my life, how could I be sure this was the right one? I prayed to my mother for help and guidance.

We moved into Steve's house earlier than planned and I managed to find a job in Exeter's Art Centre – the wages were crap and the people were distant. I have a feeling they thought I was stuck up. I had a CV to die for and here I was answering phones in the Arts Centre. I hated my job and I hated the countryside. I was a city girl stuck in the boglands.

Steve had become very quiet and seemed uninterested in me – we had not made love for a couple of months – all he did was watch telly, work and sleep. This wonderful man who had saved me from Mehmet had now become so boring I hated spending time with him, always in front of the television. Was this another of my bad decisions? Had I once more chosen a man who didn't love me? I was doing overtime with my thoughts and evaluating each moment of our lives together. I had never been too interested in TV. I watched the news and the odd soap but living with Steve I could recite the week's TV schedule.

I was again turning to my bulimia for comfort and began to binge. Unlike Mehmet, Steve never questioned what went in the shopping trolley. I was always comparing the two of them. I knew it was unhealthy but I did it anyway.

There was also another problem: bills. Steve never paid any of them. I found myself paying for everything during those first few months: council tax, electric, telephone, the lot! He worked, put his money in the bank and that was it. I could feel the anger building up inside and I wanted to shake him into reality. I was also sure that I was not going to support him. The next bills through the door stayed on the hall table – and he ignored them! By the time the reminders came I'd had enough.

I planned to leave – I was going out to Dolores in Spain and I would decide from there what to do. I had suffered enough and would not go through it again – for any man. I called Ern and had a chat with him – we had become close and I treated him as I would a father. He asked me not to do anything hasty before talking to Steve about it – I promised.

Steve collected me from work as usual and I suggested we get a takeaway and drive to the coast. Once we had eaten and chatted about our day, I asked what was wrong and told him of my plans to leave him. He was shocked, believing that everything was fine between us!

"Steve, you haven't as much as kissed me in the past month! Our sex life has been non-existent since the move to Devon!"

"I had no idea! I thought we were fine!"

"You never noticed that we don't talk or have sex?"

"Not really!"

"Come on, Steve, how stupid do you think I am? I am running your life right now but it's over. I can't look after you when I need some looking after myself. What the hell is wrong with you? For God's sake, tell me – have I done something? Are you sorry you brought me here? What's the problem?"

"Look, ever since we moved into the house I have felt strange – I am tired all the time and unaware of what's around me. I have no idea why."

"You must have some idea why you're behaving this way?"

"I think it's the house – when I lived there last my ex had left me and I became very depressed – then I went to Australia and this is the first time since I left that I have been back. It might be the house, I don't know, but I do love you and don't want you to leave me. Tell me what I have to do to make things right again?"

"I love you too and don't want to go but there is no way I will ever allow another man to treat me badly. If you want to try again, then tomorrow we go to the bank and open a joint account for the bills. We'll each put the same amount in every week. And then we have to have a social life – I am not sitting watching TV forever. If you are willing to try then I will stay but only for a trial period."

"That's fine with me. I had no idea, I swear to you, how I was behaving. I love and cherish you, Jen, and I will do whatever it takes to make our relationship work."

I then went on to tell Steve that I was an active bulimic. It took a couple of hours to explain how it all began and discuss why it still carried on but by the end Steve understood me a little bit better and we agreed to tackle the problem together.

As promised we went to the bank and set up the account. Our sex life was back on track and now all that remained was to banish the ghosts of Steve's past, but how? We could not afford to move and buy another place so I decided to redesign, removing all evidence of his ex. I put my mark on our new home and it was the most enjoyable thing I had ever done – making this house ours.

The revamp worked and we continued our happy loving relationship as before. I would often take a moment to check I was not dreaming this life. Steve and

I both worked with the bulimia. I told Steve every time I felt the need to purge and we talked it through until the urge passed. I was most certainly not cured yet but I was in control. I was now in such an idyllic situation after my past it seemed unbelievable. My divorce eventually came through and we celebrated all weekend.

After the move from London I told Honor and Daddy, if Mehmet called, to say I had gone to Scotland. He called as I had expected and they said, as promised, that I lived in Scotland. Mehmet called quite a bit and his calls were getting too much for my sister and father so I took the number he had given them and called him – careful to dial 1471 first so he could not trace the call.

"Hi, Mehmet, it's me, Jennifer. My dad wants you to stop calling him and I would like if you could leave him alone also."

"Really? Where the fuck are you, you bitch? I waited two hours for you – how dare you treat me like this – you are still my wife, remember?"

"Actually, I am not. If you check with your mother you will see the divorce is final – the papers were sent to Turkey – it was the only address I had for you."

"Then I need you to go to the Turkish embassy and sign a paper – it's urgent."

I had forgotten that our marriage was registered in Turkey and he would need a divorce there too in order to marry again. Suddenly the ball was in my court.

"What papers do you need me to sign?"

"A divorce declamation. As you know, I need your permission to make it legal."

"I am sure you can do something. After all, I got my divorce without your signature."

"You know Turkish law is different and my mother has a bride for me, waiting to marry."

"God, that's awful. Tell you what? Why don't you just piss off and leave me and my family alone? Turkey is your problem not mine, and I will do nothing to help you – ever!"

"You good-for-nothing stupid bitch –"

I slammed the phone down with Mehmet in full rant – it felt great – I was free at last. Mehmet was no longer in my life. He did phone my dad once more and gave up after that. I never heard from him again – he was gone.

20

I settled into life in Devon although I hated country life but I was happy enough at home to make up for it. Steve's childhood friend was dating a girl called Cheryl at the time and we built a friendship that continues today. I loved her parents who are healers and the most wonderful happy people you could meet. Cheryl and I had similar mindsets and gelled well.

I'd left the Art Centre and I had a job in a shoe company, selling bridal shoes – I had gone from organising weddings to selling the shoes on the bride's feet! The job was OK and the people were nice enough but I was never truly accepted. I was still 'the Irish girl from London with the big jobs'. I am sure people didn't believe me when I talked about my past. Meeting Lady Diana and Fergie were the moments of my life that most excited me at that time – I loved talking about them if ever they came up in conversation. The women I worked with just sat and stared at me when I spoke about them, so I gave up and just went along with their conversations. I cringe now when I think about it! I couldn't have normal conversations with people. They would find me a freak. Abusive marriage – eating disorder – messed-up kidneys – running from Turkey – then London? Jesus, I lived it, and still find it all so unbelievable! Until now only close friends knew my story and I was happy keeping things that way.

Steve proposed to me in Gino's Italian restaurant on June 16th 1995, almost a year after we met. I was so happy I accepted straightaway.

The proposal went like this:

"Jen, have you a pen?"

"No, not that I know of."

"Try your handbag, will you?"

"What do you want a pen for?"

"Just have a look and see, will you?"

I opened my bag and there was the little navy velvet box. Inside it held the most beautiful solitaire engagement ring.

"I love you, Jen. Will you please marry me?"

"What? No bended knee? I'm not sure I can accept if you don't get on your knee."

Steve was a very shy man and I was only playing with him – but he thought I was serious.

"Please don't make me get on my knee – I will die with embarrassment. Now, are you going to marry me?"

"Of course, I will – how could I say no to such a well-planned proposal? I mean, asking for a pen! I bet that has never been done before!"

By now we were both laughing. He had been planning for days how to give me the ring and just handing it to me in the restaurant was out of the question. People might see him! It was Steve's shy manner that had attracted me to him in the first place and I would have been shocked if he had proposed the normal way.

The wedding date was set for August 9th 1996. Everyone was delighted for us and the aura of joy surrounding me must have been contagious. I wanted to marry in the church this time and make it real. We would marry in the church I had received all my sacraments in: Christ the King, Salthill. In order to do this I had to get a letter from the Pope giving me permission as I had been married before. Even though it had been a civil ceremony I had to receive my letter of freedom from the Pope.

We set about arranging the wedding – well, I did – and out of the blue I discovered I was pregnant! It was October '95 and the baby would be born before the wedding. But within twenty-four hours the baby had gone! I went to hospital with my pregnancy test in hand and explained I started bleeding that morning. The scan confirmed what I already knew. As this was my third miscarriage, I was referred for tests.

I first saw Mr Collie in the Heavitree hospital and after a couple of invasive scans I was told it was very unlikely I would carry a child full term. In among all the other medical crap, I had endometriosis and polycystic ovaries. I wanted to die on the spot. My body was failing me. I was now to remain childless forever. I told Steve he could call off the wedding, that I would understand, but he assured me he loved me and having a child did not matter as long as we were both together. We did what so many infertile couples do and got a dog.

Tasha was the most adorable springer spaniel puppy and in many ways helped me cope with the loss I felt inside. Tasha was always happy to see me and I her. She was a spoilt puppy and got up to all sorts – she brought laughter to me and healed the pain for a little while.

One of Steve's friends had just had a baby and we went to visit. Seeing the tiny little baby in the cot brought back the longing to be a mother. I yearned to hold a child of my own but Mr Collie's words were whispering in my mind all the time. When we got home I cried. The tears were coming, flowing, as I tried to expel the emotions I felt – regret, anger and most of all loss.

I took Tasha into bed with me that night but it was no good. I longed to be a mother and it would never happen. I was worthless.

I threw myself into planning the wedding and before I knew it we were packing to go to Galway. We had only a week left and we would be man and wife. We drove and my wedding dress was laid out in the back seat, well concealed so Steve could not see it.

I was so excited about walking down the aisle and Steve seeing me in my beautiful dress, I had forgotten to pack the Pill but thought: "What the hell, I can't carry a child anyway so why do I bother?" I had planned my period for the two weeks before we married – that was the great thing about the Pill – you can stop or plan your period at will.

I became very forlorn during the lead-up to the wedding. I wished my mother was with me to choose the dress, flowers, cake and those little touches only a mother can bring. I had messed up and never given my relationship with her a chance. I had been so consumed with my feelings of uselessness and if I had only spoken out it would all have been so different. I knew now when it is too late how much she loved me and that she would have protected me from the demons.

I sat and cried when I thought back to the kitchen scene before my birthday photograph, the kiss curl that was only complete after a kiss. If I had the time all over again I would have done it so differently, or would I? Hindsight is easy; we would all change the past if given the opportunity. Go back and undo that embarrassing memory of the night you kissed the creep at the school disco? For me, to go back I would have to relive an entire childhood.

I imagined that on my wedding day my mother would be there smiling. I had this time got it right. Mam had wished so many times throughout her life that we had a painter in the family. After another of my brothers had botched a decorating job, you would hear her sigh: "If only one of them was a proper painter!" Every two years she suffered the same fate, as the house was decorated. A splash of paint here and there would really annoy her and the lads used to find it all rather funny. "Who is going to see it? Sure it's under the bed, behind the wardrobe . . ."

Mam would just sigh and try to forget about it. It's funny but when we used to help move the beds in the guest-rooms there were always paint-stains on the carpet!

Mam might be dead but she had got her painter son-in-law!

Once I got home there was so much to do: flowers, bridesmaids, church, the lot! My friend Cheryl and her mum had come for the wedding and helped me make the bouquets. I wanted a wild look, none of this fashioned overpriced bunch of flowers for me! I went for seasonal flowers tied with string. Thanks to Cheryl and her mum they looked amazing. Steve is a big West Ham fanatic and I planned the wedding colours around the team: everything was claret, blue and white from the flowers on the cake to my bouquet.

Steve's parents arrived, of course. It was a great thrill for Ernest to be in Ireland. I remember being quite shocked to find an Englishman so well versed in Irish history the first time I met him. He knew it all from the tribes to the Famine to the Rising. He could roll off names of Irish heroes I had never before heard of! I was the Irish person with a little history stored away in some mental compartment from my schooldays. I felt quite silly when Ernest spoke about some leader or another! He educated me on my history. And I introduced him to the culture. In the early days I was sitting up late one night with Ern having a drink when he told me he wished Steve and I would stay together and take him to Ireland. A long-time wish of his. Ern's wish came true some two years later. He was in his element and was extended the traditional Irish welcome, a hot whiskey with my father. I stood with my back to the sink in Dad's kitchen watching these two men talk about the old days. It was as if they had known each other forever. I was so proud that my father and father-in-law were enjoying a hot whiskey together. If only my mother could have been there, then the scene would have been complete.

We met with the parish priest a few days before our big

event and everything was in order. The pre-marriage course had been done in Exeter and I had the cert for the priest to confirm this, as well as the contract Steve had to sign promising to bring up any children we might have as Catholics! How ironic! Otherwise it was all go for Friday at 2.30.

We had the hen and stag do's on the Tuesday night, giving us both a couple of days to recover. The girls and I had a ball. I sang, danced and laughed the night away.

Poor old Steve was another matter altogether. My brother Andy and his sons tarred and feathered him – or, rather, treacled and feathered him – then walked him up and down Salthill on a dog-lead. When I saw him I almost wet myself laughing. Andy went so far as to put the event on the beginning of our wedding video but it was all good fun. I was really beginning to feel part of the family again and I was happy.

The morning of my wedding came and I found myself in line waiting for the shower. Surely the bride takes priority? But no, I was only Jennifer and I could wait.

The phone rang and it was the parish priest.

"Hi, Jennifer, we have a problem. I don't have your letters of freedom and I can't marry you without them."

"You had everything on Tuesday evening so where are they now? How can we not get married today? Everyone is here; the hotel, band and cars are arranged. You can't just tell me at ten o'clock on the day of my wedding you lost the letters!"

"We can have a blessing in the church today and I can marry you once I have the letters."

"No way, Father! I gave you everything on Tuesday and the wedding will go ahead today. It's up to you to sort it out!"

I put the phone down and went ahead as planned.

I got in the shower eventually and the water was cold. Daddy's house was old and the water-heating system for the shower took forever so I went ahead in the cold shower.

I went down to the hairdresser's and hated what she did, so back home I did my own hair and make-up.

The priest arrived and had good news: everything was sorted and the wedding was going ahead. I was pretty rude and told him it was going ahead anyway.

I had to deal with all the flower girls. I had four, as I did not want to leave anyone out. Every child in the family had a task at the wedding. I was standing looking at the clock, thinking here I was dealing with the kids and the house full of people. I let rip.

"This is my wedding and not one of you is helping! I am going to get ready and, between you, you can sort out the kids! It's the least you can do for me!"

My feelings of resentment were coming back. The only person to help me since I came home was Honor. I was just there as far as everyone else was concerned. They were all just looking after themselves and looking forward to the day out.

Honor helped me put on my wedding dress and my heart ached. I would have given anything for my mother to be there with me at that very moment.

My brother Brian had the job of taking me to the church. He had borrowed a nice flash car from the garage where he works. I closed the door and headed off to begin my new life with Steve.

Dad was unable to walk down the aisle so Andy stepped in. As I took his arm and began to make my way down the aisle, I could see Steve standing on the right of the altar looking as if he was about to be executed! The first thing I noticed was he was wearing the wrong suit! Graham our best man was about 6'1" and Steve is 5'8". The shop sent out two suits in Graham's size. I had to hold in the laughter as I drew nearer. He looked a sight but I loved him and that was all that mattered.

Andy handed me over to my father at the altar so that he could give me away. I felt so proud as I held Daddy's arm for those few moments. I was his daughter and he was about to give my hand in marriage to the man I loved. As you can see, I get very sentimental about my wedding day. Everything that could go wrong went wrong but none of it mattered.

The reception was wonderful, especially the Irish dancers that Andy had hired as a wedding present. They did the whole *Riverdance* bit and we were all on a high at the end.

Our first dance I dread to say was to 'Love Is All Around'. It was the big hit in '94 and every time I sat into Steve's car when we first met he had it set up to play on his tape.

I could not have been happier but all too soon the time came for us to go home and back to work.

Steve was completely enthralled with Irish life and wanted nothing more than to live in Galway, I on the other hand was filled with dread at the very thought of coming back to where it all began. The subject was discussed a few times and thankfully forgotten.

21

A couple of weeks after returning to Devon I made an appointment with my GP. I found making love very painful all of a sudden and although a friend said I was suffering from 'Honeymoon Syndrome' I decided to get it checked out anyway. Dr Fiona Holden saw me that day – she was one of the doctors at my local practice. She at first agreed with my friend but on examination I was told that my endometriosis was the cause. She felt that it might have become more severe and suggested referring me back to Mr Collie. All I could think was: 'This useless body of mine is letting me down again! Will I ever be free of doctors?'

The following Sunday I had a niggling feeling and convinced Steve to take me up to Tesco. Living in the sticks like we did, every outing was a long journey. I bought what I wanted, then went back home and into the bathroom. I sat on the loo and opened my newly purchased pregnancy test. I followed the instructions and left it on the sink for the two minutes. I sat staring at the bath, thinking this was the only thing in the house that we had not removed from the past. I wondered if Steve ever sat here and thought about it. I filled my head with all sorts of nonsense – anything to avoid looking at the test results. After about ten minutes Steve knocked at the door to see if I was OK. I had no choice but to pick up the little white stick and there in the middle was the pink square – there was no doubt I was pregnant! Suddenly I felt dizzy. All the emotions of the past flooded back – my lost children. The pain of losing them overwhelmed me and I sat down. I could not go through it all again. "Please, God, let me keep this child!' I begged as I sat in the peach bathroom.

I told Steve through the closed bathroom door. "I'm pregnant! I forgot to take the Pill to Ireland and now I'm pregnant. What if I lose the baby, Steve? I can't go through this again!"

"Jen, open the door, please!"

"I want to die, Steve! How could I have let this happen – the doctor said I can't carry full term! I can't do this again – I know it will kill me to have to experience the pain of losing another child!" By this time I was crying snotty tears and gasping for breath in between each painful sob.

"Jen, please let me in!"

I opened the door and fell into Steve's open arms. He had never seen me like this before – the last time I lost our baby he went off playing golf and I wept in secret.

"I don't want you to get over-excited about this, Jen – tomorrow we will go and see the doctor and take his advice. If needs be you can rest all the way through the pregnancy."

The poor bloke hadn't a clue. My horrible sick body

purged babies as I did my food – if I stood on my head for nine months it would still happen. No doctor could stop my body rejecting this child. I was a worthless human being – unfit to deliver a child into the world.

I spent the rest of the day on the sofa in Steve's loving arms. I would cry every now and then and Steve would hold me tighter, telling me how much he loved me. For a few minutes I would feel safe, then I would hit reality once more. We both went to bed emotional wrecks that night. Within minutes I had Steve snoring next to me and I felt angry with him for sleeping – why is he not awake and feeling the panic with me? Eventually I too slept – I was worn out from crying and sleep took me suddenly.

I dreamt the most beautiful dream that night. I sat holding a newborn baby – I could see the love in my face as I gently kissed the child's head and held the small perfect hand. Looking up, I saw my mother smiling at me – it was a smile of reassurance – everything was going to be fine. I woke and I was happy – I knew I was going to prove the medical experts wrong and deliver this child I was carrying.

Steve on the other hand had not had my dream and tried to convince me of reality.

"Just because you had that dream doesn't mean everything will be fine – make an appointment with the GP and we will both go this evening after work – we need his advice."

"Steve, stop panicking – everything is going to be OK, I promise you."

"You know you can't make that promise – we have to talk to the doctors. Now, will you call and make an appointment or will I?"

"I'll make the call now. Can't you just try and be happy? You are going to be a daddy next year so you'd better get used to it!"

"Jen, stop the shit talk and don't be getting your hopes up – you could end up an emotional wreck if you lose the baby – now be sensible and wait until we see the doctor!"

"God, you're so negative!" I said, forgetting how negative I had been the day before. "Can't you at least try and be happy – I am pregnant and unless I was abducted by aliens you're the daddy!"

"Just make the damn appointment!"

I phoned the surgery as promised but not to see the doctor – I made an appointment with the midwife. Steve was really angry with me! I was so convinced about this pregnancy no one could tell me about the dangers of the past. I just knew. I had made peace with my mother before she died and I had a feeling she was helping me from heaven. I found Steve on her anniversary and not only was he the kindest person I had ever met, he was the painter she'd wished for! She had got her painter son-in-law and I got the wonderful husband she always prayed I would have.

After a few days of Steve going on, I went to our GP to keep him happy. Dr Leete could promise us nothing.

"These reports from Mr Collie say you have endometriosis and polycystic ovaries which he felt contributed to your previous miscarriages."

"But that was then! I just know that I will deliver this child – I don't know how I know but I can just feel it." Besides, I knew there was no Mehmet around now to do damage.

"Well, all I can do is keep a close eye on you and see if

Mr Collie can see you asap. For now it's in God's hands."

"I am telling you I will deliver this time – I know it."

"I really hope so, Jennifer, and I am here for you both whenever you need me."

A few weeks later I had a bleed at work and almost passed out when I saw the red liquid in the loo. "Please, God, no, not again!" I phoned Steve at work at the factory and he came and got me. Dr Leete, true to his word, met us at the house – we had to drive the fourteen miles home first, but he was waiting when we arrived. By then the bleeding had stopped and all we could do was wait. I refused to go to hospital. I needed to be alone to cope if the worst happened.

I had begun to have severe evening sickness. Like clockwork every evening I was head down the toilet bowl. Memories of my bulimia came flooding back and I wondered if maybe I was doing this myself in some sub-conscious way? After all I had reached the stage years ago when I could purge without any assistance. I am sure this thought ran through Steve's mind but he never said.

We saw Mr Collie the following week and there on the screen was a blob, a white mass that was to become my child. That blob was the most precious part of my body and I would love and care for it all the way.

I was scanned every two weeks. Due to the position of my kidney auto-transplant, my kidney was blocking the view and I had to have what they call 'trans-vaginal" scans which loosely translated means they had to stick a probe inside me. The up-side was that we had a perfect view of the baby and so, unlike most mothers, I was privileged to see a miracle at work. My blob became an alien then a tiny human. I watched as the whole body developed and I loved it. Each fortnight I was a little anxious just in case I had a repeat of Shauna.

To avoid any problems Steve and I had a list of don'ts, number one of which was 'No Sex' – a bit difficult when you are newly married but we had to abstain.

I remember lying there, watching as a condom was put on the probe for hygiene reasons. It is difficult not to laugh when you see the doctor do this.

One day, I just had to ask. "If it's OK for you to put that massive thing inside me, why can't I make love to my husband?"

The doctor looked at me and we both burst out laughing. Thankfully she saw the funny side of my question, otherwise I could have had someone go into a detailed explanation as to why sex and the trans-vaginal probe are worlds apart.

"You know, once we get you to four months it is fine to have gentle sex."

"You know, I don't care how frustrated I get. I would rather have the baby at its proper due date and I know Steve feels the same."

"There are ways, you know."

"I do but I honestly only feel like chocolate and a book at the end of the day – just the thought of anything else make me feel sick."

"You better not tell Steve that!"

The two of us had the giggles, making it very difficult to do the scan. We had to try a few times before the two of us held it together long enough.

Steve was just as excited about our baby as I was and very soon into the pregnancy I'd had to force him to calm down. I am not and never have been the type to be fussed over and Steve had taken pampering to a whole other level! It's one thing having your pillows plumped but the constant asking 'Are you OK, Jen?' was driving me demented.

The evening sickness continued and I found that I was able to exist on boiled sweets. My weight loss was beginning to worry my GP and he discussed sending me into hospital. I made it clear I would go in only if I had no other choice. I went home with stuff to put in my drinking water. It was disgusting but for the baby's sake I managed to drink it. Just writing about it makes me feel sick.

When I first told everyone at work, I was met with an uneasy disbelief! I had to bear in mind I had told them only a few weeks before I could not have children and now here I was pregnant! I tried to explain but found my explanations only led them to believe I had lied in the first place so gave up. I had never been accepted fully – after all, I was 'the Irish one from London with all the big jobs'. I often found my life unbelievable so why should others believe me? I was thirty-one and by then had experienced so much and lived so many lives – how could this happy woman whose love for her husband was written all over her face have been that person? I often wish I knew the answer but I never will know.

Working throughout my pregnancy was hell. I was so happy to be pregnant and Steve was delirious yet my hormones made me cry at the slightest thing. I was tearful and the women with no children were not the slightest bit interested in my kicks and bumps. Only two of the older woman at work made the journey a little more bearable. I would often walk to the car, open the door and let the floodgates open I had managed to force shut all day. I could not afford to leave work and felt that was what the management wanted anyway – so I would put up with all the crap that is a small factory environment until I was due to begin my maternity leave.

My first kick was the most beautiful feeling and the most frightening all at once. Soon after I began to feel movement, the doctors decided to stop the scans. I was so disappointed when I was told there was no need for further scans.

My evening sickness had passed and I ate my first meal on Christmas Day. I also developed a longing for chocolate and pizza so overpowering I would panic if I was running out of either.

Eventually, after what seemed like years waiting, I went on my maternity leave. It was with great joy I left the shoe factory behind. My job in sales was not the problem – it was a couple of the managers who had changed so much once I announced I was pregnant that had made my position there so unbearable. I stuck it out and left holding the most beautiful basket that Penny and Barbara, two of the women I worked with, had put together for me.

I had not had any problems with my eating disorder since Steve and I married, but sitting at home alone all day was not easy. I was scared and lonely. I hated living in a small village with nothing more than a post office/shop. I was a city girl through and through; living in the sticks was not my idea of fun. Like all mums-to-be I could cry over an advert on the TV, so insane were my hormones, and my head was filled with all sorts of scenarios with regard to the baby's birth. What if it all goes wrong and the baby dies? Thoughts like this made keeping my bulimia at bay almost impossible – but I managed with sheer will and love of my unborn child. It was almost a year now since I had last purged, I had put weight on and like all pregnant women at near nine months I felt like a house.

The baby had a new game these days: dancing on my kidney! I could be walking down the high street when I would let out a loud cry! And as soon as I went to bed the baby decided to play bounce.

Soon enough, after two false alarms, I was in labour.

There had been lots of conversations between doctors when I was pregnant. I was the first renal auto-transplant patient they had ever come across. I knew I had been the first but seven years later I was still a freak! After phone calls and letters it was decided that natural delivery was best! If they had asked me, I know what I would have said: "Knock me out and wake me up when it's all over, please!" It seemed that due to the positioning of my kidney a Caesarean was a no-go – unless it was an emergency. When I heard this I just sat and looked at the doctor with the words 'Freak! Freak!' shouting in my head.

Steve had a very large white board with a list of 'what to do' at the end of our bed. When I woke at about three, that Friday morning, I didn't bother waking him. I was uncomfortable and in no mood for his mad panic. I went and filled a bath, knowing it would be hours yet before anything happened. I woke Steve around six and as I expected he panicked! As we prepared to go into Heavitree Maternity hospital there was a knock on the door. Our grumpy git of a neighbour was ranting about the noise my bathwater made while draining out! I told him I was in labour and he couldn't care less – so I closed the door.

I arrived at the hospital at eight only to be sent home again! It was another thirteen hours before I was admitted! Then I was no sooner settled with the monitor on when labour stopped – I was three centimetres dilated so I was sent upstairs to the ward to wait. Saturday afternoon the labour began again for a few hours – then stopped. I was sent upstairs to the ward again. By Sunday morning I had enough and was about to blow, when the midwives decided to break my waters. The baby still decided not to rush out – I was a further sixteen hours and four minutes in full labour before she arrived. At 5.04 a.m. on the 9th of June I was handed a beautiful bundle – the one I had earlier sworn to drag out of me! Keira, my little girl, had arrived – not without a fight – but I had her in my arms safe and warm. Her heart-rate shot up in the last few minutes of labour – it was an emergency delivery, one that meant I had to have a suction cup inserted to pull the little mite out. I had decided on a partial epidural so I could move around – it sounds great but in no way does it give you a pain-free labour. I know it was painful but I honestly can't remember a thing about it. I just know it hurt. I guess it's true about forgetting labour once it's over. I had her now and that was all that mattered. I would have agreed to anything just to hold her – my dreams were answered.

I was a little unnerved at first. Keira had the same dark eyes as Shauna had. I took a sharp breath, then shrugged it off. This was Steve's child and he too had dark brown eyes – mine are blue so it makes sense that Keira would have her daddy's dark eyes. Mehmet was long gone in my past. I would sometimes dream of what he had done to me and at times if I were eating something particularly fatty I would remember the taunts: 'Fat ugly bitch!'. Even today I panic if I have overeaten and then I can hear him. I gather I always will. He became so tied in with my eating disorder that it has acquired his voice.

I sent Steve home around 6.30. He had been with me for twenty-four hours at that stage – and he looked it!

A couple of hours after Keira's birth one of my midwives noticed that my urine bag was empty. I'd had a catheter inserted during the birth. The doctor decided more fluids were needed. I looked at my hands – they were very swollen. I knew from all my time with transplant patients that this was not a good idea. Too much fluid and I would drown! I fought the doctor to prevent another litre of fluid being hung – I even pulled out the needle in my hand. I don't swear a lot but I was very abusive to her. She gave up and called in a consultant. One injection and everything was working again – I was mortified by the way I behaved but I had no choice. Here I was, a mum for the first time in my life, and it could all have been so different if I had kept quiet. I did find the doctor later on the ward and apologised. I felt ashamed at the way I had spoken to her – after all, she had been with me all night, right through to Keira's birth. We had got along so well and then I ended up shouting at her at a time when she truly believed she was helping me. I was an unusual patient and it was a situation where I knew more than the doctor.

I took Keira home the Thursday after she was born. Steve and I were like little kids with a new toy. He was terrified of Keira and I was delighted to be a mum. There was a knock on the door and I opened it – to find my GP Dr Leete standing there.

"I am here to see the miracle," he said, and walked in.

I only then realised I had proven the doctors wrong. I was a mother against the odds.

The poor child is lucky she is stable after her first few days with us. We spent forty minutes on the phone to Steve's mum one evening, as we were afraid to cut her nails! I gave up and bit them! We were nervous wrecks. I was afraid of every bug or illness. Having lost Shauna I was obsessed with cot death, so much so I hardly slept for the first week – only when my body collapsed in exhaustion did I sleep and even then it was against my will. All the worry took its toll on me and a routine blood test revealed my count was so low a transfusion was on the cards. I was having none of it and agreed only to take strong iron tablets. I had a foul taste in my mouth for the duration – the tablets were disgusting. I put up with it rather than be separated from my precious child.

By the time Keira was ten days old the Catholic guilt set in. I had a voice in my head telling me babies should be baptised during the first month. I must have heard it at school or something. I booked the boat and we set off for Galway. I wanted Keira baptised in the same church Steve and I had married in, eleven months earlier. I was like a madwoman on a horse during the drive home; I wanted to kick hard to make the time and mileage go faster. Eventually we pulled up outside my parents' house and in the back seat of our car was my precious bundle.

I was so very proud walking into Mammy's kitchen, holding my daughter. Daddy was sitting in his chair and held Keira close when I laid her in his arms. She was named 'Devon Cream' by Dad and he called her nothing else from then on.

I don't know if it was the excitement of my new life or my desire to fit in but I was treated very differently during my visit. Maybe it was because I was a mother now and no longer the younger sister, who knows? I was treated with respect by all the family and for the first time in my life people listened to me. I'd had a taste of it when I married Steve but this was different. I was now a person in my own right and treated accordingly. I loved my dad and missed my mother. I was confused by all the new feelings in my head.

Steve thought my family were great and Ireland was heaven – he still wanted to move here. But I was still too afraid of what might happen and tried to put him off.

"Jen, you're a married woman and mother – it won't be like before – I will make sure of it."

"You have no idea how this all works – one wrong word and we would be outcast – trust me, I know."

"And if that happens you have me – it's Galway I love – and as for your family, if they like us one week and not the next, so what"

"I don't know. Maybe they have changed. Let's have Keira baptised and go back to Devon and talk about it all."

"That's fine by me. We'd have a house to sell and lots of loose ends to tie up, before we could move anyway. All I want you to do is think about it."

"OK, I will – but don't try to force me into coming back – I know what can happen if it goes wrong. You have to trust me."

We went to see the priest later that day. The only time he could carry out the baptism would be July the 9th at

2.30. Exactly eleven months since we had married. Keira would also be one month old that day. As a believer in fate I was so sure this was a good omen.

The service was simple but beautiful. I could relax now that the baptism was over. Everything would be OK – my daughter was safe.

We packed up and went home a couple of days later. I promised to consider life in Ireland and Steve promised not to push me.

Back in Devon we were still over-cautious with Keira. If she so much as coughed, it was up to the doctor. We went on like this for ages.

I noticed one day Steve never took Keira out. He took Tasha the dog out religiously, every day when he got in from work. Keira was eight weeks by then and I was so tired. I did everything for Keira and Steve. I was lucky to get in the shower before midnight.

He was about to get a shock. I was on the phone to Honor, ranting on about how he left it all to me, when I saw his car. I had it all planned and as soon as he came in I handed him the baby in her shoulder carrier and told him to take her out for an hour – while I had a shower and a rest.

"I need some time on my own. You come in every day, have a coffee and disappear for hours with the dog. Well, guess what – the dog can bloody wait! You are taking your daughter out while her mother, your wife, has some much-needed time to herself!"

"OK, keep your cool – what's brought all this on?"

"Let me see? Keira is two months old, you're out at work all day and I never get a break. There is a clue there for you!"

"No need to be so smart!"

"Smart! Steve, you come home and disappear with the dog every single day. Has it ever so much as crossed your mind I might need a break? Feck the dog – she won't die if she has a few days without a walk. You are not only leaving it all to me, you're also losing quality time with Keira."

"I had no idea."

"Don't talk shit! No idea? Who did you think was doing everything? It most certainly wasn't you!"

"Calm down, woman! I will take Keira out and you have a bath and relax for a couple of hours."

I handed him the baby-bag and off they went. A new mother with raging hormones is not a force to be reckoned with. I had my much-needed bath, cup of tea and a read of the newspaper. I found myself clock-watching after an hour. I waited anxiously until they returned.

Then Keira went down for a sleep and Steve and I had our first proper conversation in two months.

It turned out Steve was terrified of being alone with Keira! It was all 'what if?' – "What if I hurt her or drop her?" I had forgotten that he had no experience with babies. I on the other hand had been an aunty since I was a child – babies were second nature to me. I wasn't long showing him and we cared for her together until he had the confidence to give her a bath and get her ready to take for a walk. He would still panic every so often but soon got over it.

Soon Steve was loving being a dad and sure enough Keira's first word was 'Daa-diee!'. I was insulted for a bit but 'Maa-m-m!' soon followed.

I decided not to return to work and to spend the first three years at home with Keira. Steve had been self-employed for sixteen years; he had a good business as a painter and decorator. Money had not been a big issue for us; we always had enough to get by. Then out of nowhere the work began to dry up; meeting our mortgage payment became a bit of a struggle. Steve was now home more often than at work. What we had saved over the years was slowly being eaten up by bills. For the first time in my life I was in debt. I was horrified. Ernest, Steve's dad, had been a financial advisor and tried to keep us afloat. We managed for five months. Ernest decided we should declare bankruptcy, before the banks foreclosed on us. I was never so afraid in my life. We could end up homeless! I cried so much during that few months. The bulimia also reared its ugly head.

I had begun having health problems when Keira was three months old. Every time I had dinner I was in the most agonising pain. I would often vomit while screaming in pain. The doctors decided I had a pulled muscle in my shoulder – all the pain was high up in my back. This went on for months. I was on very strong painkillers – so strong in fact they were taken off the market. Postnatal depression was being bandied around a bit! I let my doctor know in no uncertain terms that I was not depressed. The mystery was solved in January, when I went pure yellow.

My GP could see only me outside of working hours. He knew I'd had jaundice as a child – it was possible I was now infected with hepatitis! He admitted me to hospital on the spot. I had to leave my precious child – I was dying inside. Tests soon confirmed I had gallstones!

One was now stuck in one of the ducts of my liver! I was once more wheeled into surgery but I had Steve and Keira waiting for me which made all the difference. The surgeon removed the stone and sent me home after five days – five of the most painful days – separated from my daughter. I was sure Steve was not coping and was almost jealous when I realised he was!

I was booked in to have my gall bladder out at the end of March; until then I had to cope with the medication. With the stress of our financial problems, my health and parenthood I was a mess.

We had no choice but to go to court in February '98 and declare ourselves bankrupt before the banks did. I stood in the judge's chambers holding Keira, with tears running down my face. The judge looked and me and smiled, saying: "I don't hang people on Fridays." Judge Moon treated us so well and sympathised with our situation. I owed only £1200 on a credit card, but had co-signed a loan for Steve's business so both of us had to declare bankruptcy together. If I did not declare myself bankrupt, then I would have to pay the bank. I was not working and had no means of paying off the money. I was at my lowest. With all that had happened in my life, I always had enough money to get by; now I had nothing! I sat in the car with Steve after leaving the courthouse, almost paralysed with fear – not for me but our child.

"What's going to happen to us, Steve? They can take the house, car, tools they consider inessential, everything!"

"We can go to Ireland and start again."

"Are you mad as well as stupid? Going back with nothing? No home, money or future. Ireland is worse than here – there is no work!"

"Andy says the place is booming. There is work everywhere."

"Andy would say anything, to get us back home. He likes you and would like nothing better than to have you around!"

"Jen, it's our only chance of starting again. We have to try."

"I don't want to go home. I don't fit in. The fighting will start within weeks. Everyone will tell me how to live my life!"

"Let's go home and talk. We have time – the banks can't make us homeless straight away."

We talked and talked: Ireland was our only hope of starting again. Steve would always be known as bankrupt here. I had no choice – it was out of my hands. I was going back to the start. We planned to go to Galway on March the 15th.

This meant I had to transfer my operation too; it could take months to get it organised. My GP stocked me up with medication.

I was an active bulimic again but Steve had no idea. With all that was happening to our lives, he hadn't the time to notice what I was up to. With all the stress, it had reared its head again after our experience in the courthouse. I felt shame and disgrace for what had happened. I believed if I had continued to work in the hotel trade we would have managed to ride the storm. Deep down, I knew my life in hotels was over when I left London – I was burnt out and could never return to that career unless it was in the office – but I just needed someone to blame and I chose myself.

I set about selling everything the liquidators couldn't

take: washing machine, dryer, the lot. Going home we would need some money to set up our new lives. The hardest part was watching my lovely Cavalier drive away to auction. We only had a few payments left on the car. I had bought it three years earlier and now it was gone! I watched as our lives were slowly dismantled – day by day a little bit more was gone. Eventually my nephew Denis, Andy's oldest son, and his girlfriend drove over in his van from Galway to help with the move. Denis had a good-sized van and we had just bought a thirteen-year-old Volvo estate. Every piece of our lives was packed into the vehicles for the long drive west.

22

We got to my parents' house around 11.30 that night. Keira had slept almost the whole way, waking for the occasional bottle. I was drawn and worn down when we arrived. I walked into the house and the welcome was warm. Honor, her husband Ray and Daddy were so happy to have us home safe.

Honor and Ray had moved into the house before my mother died to help with Daddy when he had a bout of pneumonia (something I was unaware of at the time – I was told he had a bad cold). Then they stayed on to help my mother with Mary's children and, of course, to look after my father when Mammy died.

Nine-month-old Keira settled herself in immediately and won them all over with her smile. Honor took her upstairs to a toy wonderland – they were bonded for life once she saw all the toys. John and Helen had given us all the toys their daughters had grown out of and I was eternally grateful. Helen also gave us clothes. She gave us these things not out of charity but because they had no use for them – families always pass things on to each other. I reconciled myself with this thought, worried that people would think I couldn't afford to dress my little girl.

I felt happy to be home, so much so I was amazed by my feelings that night as I closed my eyes.

The following morning we were faced with the embarrassment of signing on. I felt sure we would be looked down on, but everyone was so nice and I was in shock. Ireland had changed so much since I left. People treated us with respect and did all they could to help. Steve and I were a young couple who had fallen on hard times. Social Welfare wanted to help us find our feet once more. The fact we both had stamps probably helped also.

We had no sooner sorted out our Social Welfare when Steve got a job. Life was about to start over.

23

After two weeks in Daddy's house, we found a two-bed flat. It was horrible and smelt of damp but it was all we could afford. We moved in and did our best.

Tasha stayed with Honor and Daddy. We had no garden and the arrangement seemed to work. But Steve missed his dog and asked the landlord if we could move her in. I was fuming.

"How the hell do you think I am going to cope with a baby and a dog locked in all day?"

"All Tasha wants is water and a place to sleep. What's so difficult about that?"

"Use your bloody brain, Steve. Keira is crawling. She also rams the dog with her walker. I will have to be on guard every second of the day!"

"Tasha would never hurt Keira. Lock her in the bedroom if you're worried – she'll sleep all day."

"If you had a brain you would be dangerous. It won't work."

Daily life was difficult enough for me without the stupid dog. I loved Tasha but it was a bit much to ask me to cope with the dog and child when we had no garden. No matter how much I loved Tash, I did not trust her or any dog for that matter with a baby.

Also, I was still suffering with my gall bladder. My gall-bladder operation was booked for the end of April. I still had just over a month to live with this pain and exhaustion. I was always tired these days; it was put down to the gall bladder and parenthood. I knew it was more. I had a feeling this was the beginning of something serious.

I began to hate the dog and Steve for bringing her to the flat. All was well when she was at Dad's house – there was a garden there and a warm bed. Steve could have waited until we had saved the deposit to rent a house with a garden. I no sooner had Keira down for a sleep than the dog would begin to bark and woke her up. I was so tired and frustrated all the time, it was like pressure building up in my head waiting to explode. I was sure Steve loved that dog more than me and in my frustration I began to hate Steve.

What the hell was wrong with me? Why was I feeling this way? Was I having a breakdown? All the unanswerable questions buzzing in my head at that time.

I had my surgery and thankfully I only had to spend one night in hospital. I seemed unable to recover and woke one night to find the bed wet with pus! It seemed I had developed an abscess below the incision; it had burst in the night.

I was also a mental wreck after reading in my admission

letter that the surgeon believed I was 'morbidly obese'! My bulimic tendencies were rampant and now I was plagued with infection. I felt once more unworthy and unlovable. I slowly became an overactive bulimic once more. The baby weight had hung on. I began my pregnancy losing weight and now I was fourteen stone. It was a strange twist of fate. Fat for me equalled unhappiness yet the baby weight brought me joy, and now nine months later it was holding on for dear life. I purged every meal and survived on tea but I lost nothing. I knew this was no way to lose weight. My body was in shock and hoarding every ounce of fat. I had no idea how to diet – I only knew my eating disorder! I almost fell one day while carrying Keira to her cot and realised I was playing with fire and my health. I ate once a day from then on and believe it or not I lost a few pounds. I knew that all I had to do was eat three healthy meals and the weight would fall off me but I was incapable of doing it the right way. I always felt like there was too much food to eat in a proper diet!

I started smoking to relieve the hunger pains and stress. I had smoked for a few years before I married Mehmet but then he insisted I stop, so I only had my secret cigarettes from then on although I always smoked at home in Galway or when I was away from him. I had given up voluntarily after I married Steve and now here I was again.

Daddy had become very disabled from his arthritis and Honor was now caring for his every need. I went to the house every day with Keira and for the first time in my life I was getting to know my father. I began hounding the health department, trying to get my father's needs met.

The nurses came every two days to see him. They were invaluable with their help and advice.

I was getting more out of control with my purging all the time. I ate for a couple of days and then starved for a few more. I had just managed to find a bearable level with my bulimia, if there is such a thing, purging occasionally not daily, when out of nowhere the feelings returned. I felt worthless and unworthy once more. I hid my feelings until I had to let go.

I went to see my GP and just cried my heart out. Niamh Haverty was a caring doctor and listened to me. I told her how I had begun drugging the dog so that Keira could have her afternoon sleep! I was using the sedatives the vet gave us for the boat journey. When they ran out, I used some Valium I had found in Mammy's bedside locker. When I was at home I gave Tasha her pill at lunch-time. By the time I put Keira down the dog was dopey and couldn't be bothered barking. Tasha barked at everything. I was truly demented with her. I had put up with the barking for over a month and it was always the same. I put Keira down to bed and the dog would bark, wake her and I was landed with a cranky child. I came to my senses after talking to Niamh. The dog barked only because she was so confined. I would have to get Steve to drop her off at my dad's every morning and bring her back on his way home, or take her to work. We all loved Tash. Keira was nuts about her and she was so patient – every time she was chased by the child, she just stood there until I caught up and freed her. She too was suffering, being locked up – prior to our move she had her freedom and now she was being confined for no good reason.

I was in a two-bed extension flat with a child and large

dog – and no garden. I was constantly tired and weak. Steve didn't notice a thing. He left at 7.30 every morning and got home by six that evening. He was oblivious. At times I wanted to shake his brain.

"Can't you see what's happening here? I am not well and you don't even notice!"

Of course, I never said a word. Dinner was ready every night and Keira played with Daddy.

I was eventually hospitalised with the infection from my surgery. None of the conventional pills or potions had worked. I spent a week on intravenous antibiotics and was discharged infection-free.

I convinced Steve to drop Tasha down to Dad's every morning when I came out of hospital

"Steve, we both love Tasha but don't you think it's cruel leaving her here all day?"

"What else can we do with her? It's not fair that she should have to live away from us."

"She doesn't have to. I have spoken to Honor and Dad and you can drop her off in the morning on your way to work and collect her on your way back – sure, myself and Keira are there every day anyway."

"I never thought of that!"

The deal was done and in a way Steve thought it was his idea!

My health improved and it was summer. I could leave the flat every day and go to Daddy and Honor.

My father continued to deteriorate; he had lost the will to live when Mammy died. He was subject to chest infections and his heart and lungs were under strain.

Honor, Sandra and myself were having a job with him. He was not interested in getting better. He wanted to go to my mum.

Eventually we decided to move him downstairs to a larger room where we could care for him more easily. I got Steve to decorate a room, a downstairs bedroom that hadn't been used for years, for him. We had it rewired and heating installed, then the Health Board gave us a special bed. Dad left the room he had shared with his wife for decades, for the first time. We did our best putting pictures of Mam up for him and brought all his bits and pieces down to his new room with him. We all knew deep down that the end was near; all that could be done now was to make his life as comfortable as possible.

"What do you think of your room, Dad? I chose the wallpaper."

"It'll do."

"Is that it after all the long hours we put in? We had electricians, floor-fitters and of course the world's best painter. Surely you can say a bit more than 'it'll do'?"

"What more do you want?"

"Let me see – what about 'It's the best room I have ever seen'?"

"Whatever you say."

A man of few words, my father, but the blackest sense of humour this side of the universe. I had to measure his exact height when the Health Board were supplying us with a bed with side-bars. In I went, tape measure in hand. I decided to take it a step further. I measured Daddy's height, feet, hands, arms, the lot! He asked what I was at.

"Look, Dad, now that I know all your measurements I can get the undertakers to get your coffin ready. When you drop, all I have to do is phone and they will be straight out!"

"You really think you're smart, don't you? Get out before I throw you out!"

"And you're going to do that how exactly?"

"Go on off with you!"

When I was later accused in jest of imprisoning him in the hospital bed with sides on it, I piped back and told him I had to do something to stop him going to the nightclubs every weekend when Honor was asleep. He was giving us a bad name with all the hip-hop dancing! Daddy laughed during what I am sure was for him a scary moment – it passed in humour.

All the time we were exchanging words, you could see the fun in his eyes and the laughter on his face. Dad loved a bit of fun and once I left the room, I heard him laugh.

Around the same time that Daddy became unwell, the property developers arrived. They bought all the land and houses in front of and adjoining Dad's. I was objecting on his behalf to the proposed monster of a building they intended to build. It was going to block his daylight and God knows what else. The darn thing was planned to be nine storeys high! The planners brought it back to seven but it was still going to affect Dad's house.

But the building was going to be the least of our family problems. Developers with money can tear families apart and mine was no different. As soon as compensation was on the cards, the split began. Get Daddy to sell them the house and we can have some money. Sounds straightforward – only Daddy had the house left to Honor!

At first I joined forces with the others. We decided the house should be sold, Honor, her husband and Daddy get an apartment and we split the rest. I was broke and the money on offer would change my life. But I soon got sick of the family meetings and backstabbing. I realised how stupid we were all being. I'd had money once in my life and it brought me only unhappiness. I could see my father wanted to die in his home and I was going to respect his wishes. The fight was on.

Then Andy said I had received a backhander from the developer in an attempt to discredit me! Right, this could only have been true if I were helping them acquire the house. Considering I was against the sale, why would they give me money? During one of the family meetings, in my sister's apartment, Steve went over and asked all of them one by one if they truly believed I had received money from the developers? Each in turn nodded yes.

My sister-in-law followed him to the door. "You don't know her like we do – she's a bitch!"

I was not only disgusted but saddened. What I had believed all my life was bluntly staring me in the face, I was not one of them – I did not fit in. I only wished I had received a backhander – I would have flaunted it in their faces.

I realised my father was the important person in the equation, something the others were forgetting. There were two camps: Honor, Daddy and me versus the rest of the family. Brian stayed out of it all; he had more sense than to get involved in such crap. It took time but I managed to talk everyone round. For my father's sake.

"We have to start realising this is Dad's house. He wants to die in it. Is the money so important that we have to tear strips off each other? What little money we would get would be spent in a few months. It's not worth it. More importantly, all the going-on is hurting Daddy."

I used the same speech with everyone. It took time but they realised how ridiculous everything was in the end. All of us loved Daddy and not even money could make us hurt him in the end.

I was treated very badly during that time – many hurtful things were said which can never be taken back. I dealt with it but I am unable to forget. I so very often wish that I had the ability to just let things go out of my head, but it just won't happen. I find myself often remembering painful situations; no amount of breathing one's problems into the air, visualising or meditation will take away the memories I dearly wish I could forget. I spent my life wishing to be loved by the family; I knew after this episode that it would never happen and I no longer wanted it to. We were worlds apart and always would be.

As far as Dad was concerned, family harmony was returning once more. There was peace in the camp and he was happy. Steve and Keira on the other hand were suffering. I spent every day talking to the developers and convincing them the house was not for sale, then solicitors and finally the Health Board to make sure Dad's needs were met.

I thank God every day for the opportunity I had during

the last fourteen months of Dad's life. I got to know him like never before. He was so honest and kind. I realised that the quiet man in the corner was the knot that held us all together. I loved him so much that I began to will death to take him.

Andy and I were at loggerheads still, over the house. Daddy asked me one day to let it be. He wished to die in his house, and after that he didn't care. "You," he said, "need to look after Devon Cream."

Even my father in his state realised I was putting everything before myself and my family as usual. I began to spend more time at home and not rush to Dad's as soon as I got up and ready. I also made a point of being home every evening before Steve.

I got Keira ready every morning. We watched *Bear in the Blue House*, *Barney* and *Rolie Polie Olie*. I showered and dressed, then we set off to Daddy's house. I was really enjoying this extra time with just myself and Keira and from what I could tell so was she.

Keira loved my father. She called him 'Granand' and when he had his bed-bath she put on her oversized gloves and adult-size apron, then dowsed the poor man in powder! He enjoyed every minute. Because Dad had a hospital bed with sides I would lay her down with him every day for her afternoon sleep.

I was suffering from fatigue all the time. My new GP Dan Murphy put it down to the stress I was under. Sometimes my hands were so painful I could hardly use them! Stress seemed the obvious culprit. But I still had that gut feeling of something more.

Sometimes when I was with Daddy I would pray that I

never ended up like him, totally dependent on others for everything. What a horrible way it must be to live out one's life, I thought. I asked him one day how he was coping. I had expected him to reply with a one-word answer, such as 'Grand' but he cried. I was stuck to the spot. I had only ever seen my dad cry once before! That was in my cousin's house, the night we were told Mam would not make it. He had become distressed by his helplessness. This six-foot strong man must have hated having his daughters look after him – he was independent all of his life and now, at eighty-one, old age and arthritis had confined him to his bed.

The last couple of months were awful. Every day you knew it was nearer the end. I still wished it would come soon for him even though I had no desire to lose my father. I found the pain in his eyes almost unbearable. I had to find words of comfort as I watched this strong silent man cry!

"Daddy, you know I love you, don't you? I might have given you many sleepless nights in my time, but I have always loved you!"

I had to leave the room before I broke down. How cruel life can be, to make this giant of a man disabled. I found myself questioning the existence of God.

My health seemed to improve a bit and I was less tired. We were in Ireland for a year and Steve was never out of work. I was beginning to believe that we had made the right decision. Whatever about the family problems, we were doing well in our little unit of three. We had a routine that worked and I can honestly say I was happy. My bulimia had been pushed to the back of my mind once more. My precious daughter was thriving. Keira's life was filled with love and happiness – my sisters doted on her and Steve and I adored her. We were content.

The phone rang on the morning of May the 3rd, 1999. It was Honor.

"Daddy's not good. Can you come straight down?"

"Sure. I'll be there in five minutes. What happened?"

"I don't know. He has a cough and is hardly able to breathe."

"I am on my way."

As soon as I saw my father's face I knew: this was his last day. The room was strangely calm and my father's face seemed peaceful. Honor, who had spent the past eight years caring for Dad, knew it was the end too. She cried and tried to convince herself he had a cold. She had washed and shaved him as usual, believing all he needed was a cough bottle! But I knew she had the same feeling as I did that this was the end. Dad had called her down from bed the night before and thanked her for looking after him. They talked well into the night about the old days, the neighbours past and present.

Tasha was in residence for the weekend in Daddy's house. Dad nicknamed her 'Snatcher' as she would always steal the tissue from his pocket as he sat in his armchair. Tasha was an expert thief; Dad used to say: "If drugs were wrapped in tissue, we could give her to the drug squad!" The night before he died, Daddy shared his chocolate biscuit with Tasha; she spent the night sleeping by his bed.

I phoned the doctor. She came to the house to see my

father and confirmed that Dad had a chest infection. She called me outside.

"He hasn't long to go, a couple of days at the most."

"Will his death be peaceful?"

"I can't see why not. Your father has a condition known as COPD – Chronic Obstructive Pulmonary Disease – and his lungs are filling with fluid. He will eventually fall into a coma due to lack of oxygen, then pass away peacefully."

"I want my father to die – he has had enough and is ready. He will die today, I just know it. Are you on duty all day?"

"I am. If you need me I will come straight back. Don't be afraid to call me."

"Look, doctor, we both know the man has had enough but my sisters will lose it when he goes. It will be like the Wailing Wives of Jerusalem in there. Can you give me something for them? I don't want my father to die with tears and cries around his bed. I witnessed it once in London and I am sure the woman's death was stressful."

"They are not my patients so I can't really."

"But you're covering for my doctor too – what about writing a prescription for me?"

"If it gets worse, call me and we can see then."

She knew what I was trying to do. I am sure she had witnessed many deathbed scenes and understood I wanted my father to die in peace.

The day dragged on and my father slipped in and out of a coma. Honor was very distressed about Dad not eating any lunch.

"I don't want him to be hungry!"

"Where he is now there is no hunger," I said. "Stop making yourself stressed."

The whole McGrath family came and went all day. Daddy was in a coma by early afternoon. He sat up in the bed before he slipped away for the final time and looked at the large picture of himself and my mother, said her name "Maureen", then slowly lay down and drifted away into his coma once more. We never heard from him again. I called the doctor back around eight as his breathing became crackly. Helen's sister Rose had a nebuliser which we set up to try and clear his chest. Knowing the end is near for a loved one makes you all the more determined to try and prevent that final moment. You will try everything for a few moments more – it's a natural reaction.

I spoke to the doctor again and she said it wouldn't be long. Poor Dad struggled on until 11.30 before finally succumbing to the death he so truly desired. We were all at the bedside except Andy and Dolores. I had been trying to contact Andy for a couple of hours and Dolores was on her way home from Spain.

Once the end came the girls started. I could not understand why they were not happy for the man. Was I wrong to wish him peace? I had been holding him when he died and will forever be grateful for the honour of being present at such a peaceful death. The doctor, after witnessing the outcry of grief, gave me some pills and I managed to get Honor to take one after begging her for an hour!

Andy arrived about half one. He insisted I had not tried to phone him! I had left messages on both his mobile and house phone. He had made the decision not to be there. I warned him that the phone bill would prove me right.

He spent a bit of time in the room with Daddy, then all the crap started. I was his target: he blamed me for putting a stop to the house sale and turning everyone against him. People turned away because they'd had enough.

He stood against the fridge and began: "Let you not think you're singing at the father's funeral!"

"I can do what the hell I like – and there's nothing you can do about it!"

"Who the fuck do you think you are?"

"What's it got to do with you?"

Like children in a playground we fought, all of us in turn. Andy had poured tea into my cigarettes when my back was turned. He had no idea I had more and thought I would be left at such a trying time without them. Thinking back, I feel sickened that our father was not yet cold in the other room and all this shit was going on next door. It was unforgivable but I had a feeling my father would be smiling if he turned back to see us. Nothing had changed: the kids at the kitchen table had never grown up.

Myself, Brian and John went to choose Dad's coffin and arrange the funeral. We had the school choir sing 'Danny Boy' for him, and then sent him to rest with the woman he loved. The loss of my father was painful but made easier by the fact that he was at peace.

I found my health taking a turn for the worst in the months following Dad's death. The in-bickering had begun once more; the trusty developer had lain in wait for his chance to pounce. Once more when money came into the equation so too did unrest. The offer was upped and accepted. Honor would move into a new house, and the profit would be divided. How simple things seem! Poor Honor had twice put a deposit on a house; yet the money for Dad's house never came! Eventually the developer went bankrupt and the house remained. The pain and stress we all suffered during that time has left us all in some way further apart.

24

The summer of '99 was a strange one; Honor and I were at a loss what to do. Dad was gone yet I found the habit of going to the house every day hard to break. We took Keira to the beach and ran after her every few minutes when she made a run for the water. All Keira ever wanted was to be in the water. I had struggled with her on winter's days to try and keep her out of it. There was no such thing as building sandcastles with Keira; it was in the sea or nothing. I would bring a few changes of clothes every time we went out on the prom, as well as keeping a few in Honor's house.

For some reason that summer Andy's children, now grown-up, who would always call to see Honor, just stopped calling. We just thought that with their grandfather gone they had no reason to call. Soon all the stories began: he said, she said and the man around the corner said! Another family argument but this time it was another generation and there never was any argument to speak of.

I was past caring about any of the family crap – I couldn't care less about who was or was not speaking to me. The drama leading up to my father's death had hardened me. I was still there for people but I had changed. One day Andy's children decided that they would not talk to any of us again, and so the torch had been passed on. Not only had their father spent his life either talking or not talking to you, but I believe his children had inherited his behaviour. I feel sorry for them but couldn't care less if they talk to me or not.

I went to see my GP in the October, as I was just a complete mess. I had no energy and, as for my hands, Steve had come in from work the night before to find I had them bandaged to try and stop the pain. Dr Murphy talked about the stress I had been under – he would do a blood test to see if I was run down.

"We will see what the results are then. I will have a better idea how to treat you. I am sure it's all the stress and anxiety you've been suffering this past year."

"Dan, can you also test me for Multiple Sclerosis? I don't know why but I keep thinking about it. What exactly is it?"

"It's a disease of the nervous system. You don't have any signs of it – I can see no medical reason to suggest it."

"For years I have had it in my head that I have the disease. I saw a poster once in a Tube station and thought 'I have that'. I had forgotten about it until this morning and knew I had to ask you to test me for it."

"Honestly, Jennifer, there are no signs of something like MS. Let's wait and see what the bloods say."

"You know from my note that I have an eating disorder?"

"Yes."

"Well, I am active on and off again. I can't seem to get it under control."

"There is a new organisation called Bodywhys – you should give them a call. I have only just heard of them but I have been told they offer help and support to people with eating disorders."

"I'll phone and have a chat. Thanks."

I didn't, well, not for some time after, but I wrote down the name and number and kept it safe.

I don't think I ever went back for the results of the blood tests. The pain in my hands went – and I felt a whole lot better.

Santa was the most important thing in our house that year. Keira was two and a half, she was grasping the concept of Christmas and Steve and I loved it.

I got the flu for the first time in my life after Christmas. I had never felt so ill. Honor had to come and mind Keira every day for over three weeks. I was useless.

Afterwards I was very fatigued. Steve had to call Dr Murphy out one Saturday morning when I could not stop vomiting. I had developed a tummy bug as well as the flu. I was a total mess

"Steve, I am going to give her an injection – it will make her sleep. She needs rest. You should take Keira out for a couple of hours while she sleeps."

"It's not her bulimia then?"

"No, it's a virus and it's doing the rounds."

Dr Dan Murphy was the gentlest, most caring doctor I had ever met and I had met many. His manner and understanding made you feel that you were his only patient – and at that time you were. He had no idea then but he was to become the person who saved my sanity. I recovered and the flu seemed as if it never happened.

It took more than a month for me to regain my strength. Honor had been in care mode during that time. She looked after Keira and me every day. I am forever grateful.

25

When Gabrielle decided her marriage was over, I helped her move on and start a new life. I had become very close to her since coming home, Keira loved her girls and we went everywhere together. I could see how unhappy she was and, not wanting another woman to suffer in an unhappy marriage, I did everything I could for her.

While we were sorting things out I woke one morning unable to see. I thought I had died and was extremely annoyed that there was no one to meet me. I heard Keira breathe and knew then I was still here. After about thirty minutes the sight in my left eye began to improve. It was near normal after an hour or so and I decided I needed new glasses and got on with my day. I could see light and dark only in my right eye so I decided not to say anything to anyone. I made an appointment with the optician for the Saturday afternoon.

I went to see Dr Murphy later that day with Gabrielle – the girls were acting up and as she needed support I had hoped he would refer her to a consellor. I never thought to mention my eyes. Gabrielle had a good chat with Dan and went home armed with rules and regulations. None of which was implemented.

I went to town on Saturday and did a bit of shopping in Penny's before my eye appointment. The bloody thing was driving me crazy! Bright lights caused headaches and I felt like I had a knife through my right eye. By now the left one was back to normal so I felt it was just a slight problem, maybe an infection. I waited to be called and looked at various new frames, wondering which I would choose. I was only seconds into the examination when the optician asked me to go straight to hospital. She said I had blood on my optic nerve and needed to see a specialist.

I went to phone Dr Murphy and ask his advice, thinking the woman was mad. I guess deep down I knew it was serious and went into denial for a bit!

"Hi, Dan, it's Jennifer Banks. I have just left the optician and she wants me to go to hospital – she says I have blood on my optic nerve."

"Did you have a fall or bang your head?"

"No, I woke up not being able to see properly – on Tuesday morning. There's still something wrong with my right eye." Because the left had returned to normal after a couple of hours it seemed unimportant now.

"You were in the surgery that day – why did you say nothing?"

"I just thought I needed glasses."

"What happened to your mother again?"

"She had a brain haemorrhage – why?"

"Is Steve with you?"

"Yes."

"I want you to go to the Casualty – I will phone ahead. You need to stay calm and head straight there."

"Do you think I have had a bleed?"

"I don't know – just go to the hospital and I will phone them now."

Steve was in the Early Learning Centre playing with Keira.

"Steve, buy some paints or colours for Keira. I have to go to the hospital – now."

"Why? What's happened?"

"Look, just do what I said – we can talk in the car."

Steve bought Keira the most luminous paints – ones that don't wash out – he's a man, what can I say?

We got in the car and Keira was crying – she objected to leaving the shop.

"Steve, you have to stay calm – Dan is phoning on ahead and a doctor will be waiting for us."

"Jen, what the hell is it?"

"I have blood on my optic nerve – I may have had a small bleed."

"Is that very dangerous?"

"Well, he asked me about my mother's brain haemorrhage."

Steve was in a complete panic and I was afraid I would die at any moment. "Jesus Christ, Jen! Why didn't you tell me how bad your eye was?"

"Look, just forget all that now. I have to tell you where things are. The phone bill is due next week and it's in the side of the food cupboard. There is also the electricity bill and that's in the top drawer by my side of the bed. It only came yesterday so it's not due for a few weeks."

I looked after the household bills and I was sure I was about to die – just like my mother. Steve needed to know how to cope without me.

"Look, we'll be fine, you'll see," I said. "I know they are all panicking over nothing."

The five-minute drive to the hospital seemed like forever. I was holding a now sleepy Keira close and kissing her repeatedly, fearing I was about to leave forever. Doctor Murphy, true to his word, had phoned ahead and I was sent to the fifth floor of the hospital.

I was greeted by a woman doctor, Doctor Harney.

"I will be with you in a moment – I just need to set the room up."

"Thank you."

"Don't look so stressed. It might be a good idea to take the baby away – this is not an ideal place for her."

Steve wanted to be with me and by now Keira had sensed something and had begun to cry – we needed help. Steve and Gabrielle had had a silly falling out and now we needed her. He phoned and she came straight to the hospital to look after Keira.

I was taken into what looked like a torture chamber! Dr Harney explained that she needed to administer an anaesthetic to both my eyes and I would be totally blind for two hours or so.

When the procedure was over, and I still was blind, she told us there was no bleed to the brain but my optic nerve was inflamed. She could not say why! I had to attend a clinic on Monday morning.

Being blind is so very strange – it's like the world is just noise outside your head. I went to Honor's house and drank tea while I waited to see again. The relief of knowing I had not had a haemorrhage was tremendous – I had prayed to anyone who would listen for the last two hours – I was not going to die. For someone who wished so much for death in the past, since I had met Steve and had Keira I wanted to live – forever.

I regained my sight in the left eye, while the right saw light and dark only, as it had before I went home. (I still get double or blurred vision if I am looking at something for a long period.)

Steve and I held each other so tight that night as the fear of the afternoon still hung in the air around us.

"If I lost you, Jen, how would I go on? I love you so much and I need you – Keira needs you. We can't survive without you."

"I don't ever want to leave you – I love you with all my heart. I never want to leave you!"

The thought of leaving Keira and Steve was still raw in my heart. I'd had a close call once more. Why was my body so unhealthy? Why did it always fail me? I knew that the years of my eating disorder must have damaged me. I had to have my three front teeth crowned. And I was sure the kidney problems were linked to the abuse my body had suffered. But why this problem now? My bulimia was inactive again; I ate a healthy meal every day. Granted it was just the one but I did make sure I took supplements. So why was I still suffering?

Monday morning came and I left Keira with Honor.

I saw Dr Harney and she could see no improvement. I was to be referred to a neurologist, Dr Abdul.

"Have you seen this before?" I asked. "Please tell me the truth."

"I have but there can be many reasons for optic

neuritis. The neurologist will be able to tell you more on Friday."

"Could I have Multiple Sclerosis?"

"Yes, this can often be a first symptom of the disease."

I have no idea where my question had come from – but I knew that I had MS. Still I had no real idea what it was. I only ever knew about Douglas's Aunt Barbara and she was an old lady at the time she died. Why was I so sure I had a disease I knew nothing about? It has to have been mentioned to me before. So much was going on in my life during the dark days; when I read my medical notes I realised I had forgotten half of it. I decided to say nothing to Steve for now and wait until Friday.

It was the longest four days of my life. Every time I thought of what lay ahead I got butterflies in my stomach. I knew I had MS and I was too afraid to find out about it. Was I going to die? Would I be in a wheelchair? What if I couldn't look after Keira? So many questions and not one answer. I hated my body; it failed me at every opportunity. When I was a child I hated my chubby body – in an attempt to change things, had I set on a long road to suicide? Have I been slowly killing myself since childhood? If that was true, why was I still here? I attempted suicide, I died on the operating table, why had I survived all of these things and just when I was happy, I had MS?

In my darkest hours in the past I always used to imagine my mother's voice telling me things would be fine. Even when Keira was born, I cried because Mam was not here to see her. I could swear I heard her say, "She's beautiful!" when I was resting after giving birth. I needed to hear her now, telling me it would all be OK. No matter how hard I listened during those few days, I heard nothing!

On Friday everyone was saying: "I bet there's nothing wrong!" I heard their words but I knew the answer.

Steve and I went in to see Dr Abdul while Gabrielle and Honor looked after Keira outside in the garden. I needed everyone with me; I could not be alone, not now.

After reading Dr Harney's letter and a neurological exam he began to speak.

"Mrs Banks, I want to send you for an MRI – a scan of your brain and spinal cord – as soon as possible. That will give us an idea what is going on."

"Have you any idea what might be wrong with me?"

"It is too early to tell and we need to do some tests first."

"You must have some idea. Dr Harney mentioned MS. Do you think I have it?"

"There is a very high possibility but I can't offer a diagnosis without tests."

I was pushing him and he knew it. I was well aware that doctors more often than not know the diagnosis before the test results.

"In your judgment, do you feel I have MS and if not what could it be?"

"I would expect your tests to show you have Multiple Sclerosis, but there is a very slim chance you may have a tumour. After your examination I doubt you have one. Only the MRI can rule it out definitely."

"How long will I have to wait for the scan?"

"You will have to go to Cork for it – about six weeks I would say."

"Six weeks! You're joking? Can I go private? And have the scan faster?"

"Yes, but it will cost about two thousand pounds. I feel we can wait for the scan in Cork. There is no emergency."

"You know I have MS, don't you?"

"Mrs Banks, I have told you I can't diagnose yet. But my gut feeling is MS."

"Can I die from it?"

"It depends on whether you progress to a more serious stage of the disease. Most people don't."

"Will I be in a wheelchair and if so how long will it take to happen?"

"Most people with MS go on to live normal lives. You may never again have an episode or you could progress quickly. We don't yet know."

"Is there a cure?"

"No. But there is always ongoing research. And we do have treatments."

"What happens now?"

"Once you have your scan, call the appointments secretary and we will see you a week later. For now I suggest you go home and get on with your normal life. The more you worry, the worse it will be in the long term. If you have multiple sclerosis, this particular disease thrives on stress."

"Get on with my life? Like that's possible. My life has changed forever now. I will never again be the same."

I came out of the office and Honor and Gabrielle were waiting. They'd had to come in from the garden, they were so worried. I told them I had Multiple Sclerosis. Steve was in shock. We went back to Honor's, drank tea and sat in silence. We all decided to walk up to the shop together.

On the way back we saw my brother John in the takeaway. Steve was waiting for a chance to let off steam and at that moment John just happened to be there. He had been in my sister Sandra's apartment the Saturday night when it all started. A joke had been made about my blindness – something along the lines of: "I can see! It's a miracle!" I don't know, I wasn't there. Someone had been stupid enough to tell us the following day.

Now John asked what had happened at the hospital and Steve just stared at him saying: "What do you care?"

"What do you mean?"

"It was all very funny last week when Jen lost her sight, wasn't it? I heard what you did."

"It was a joke!"

"Well, it's not a joke for us!"

I took Steve away, then went back and said to John: "He's in shock. I have just been as good as diagnosed with MS."

Steve and John had nothing in common. They were very different men and found it difficult to communicate. It was no big problem – you can't expect everyone to be best friends, just because they have a family tie.

Today was a bad day and I got Steve back to Honor's as quickly as possible. I phoned the MS Society helpline and all they could do was send me books! I wanted answers now and nobody was giving them to me. It was Friday afternoon and I had the weekend to go before I had any hope of finding the answers to my burning questions.

I have no idea how I got through the rest of that Friday. Steve hugged and kissed me at every opportunity. I was on autopilot and carried on as normally as possible.

I cried alone – I had years of experience at hiding my feelings. I lay awake all night and went to the toilet to cry. At one point, the pain in my heart was so intense I did what I knew best: purged. In the morning I carried on as normal, inside I was dying. I had once more intense hate for my failing body. I was almost desperate for the chance to purge; it was the only way I knew to cope with pain. I loved Steve and Keira with all my heart but I knew this disease would hurt them. Maybe they would be better off without me? I was useless to anyone now. My life was over.

My brother Brian printed off some stuff from the Internet for me. I had forgotten that a member of his wife's family had had the chronic progressive form of MS and had died from it. Brian was never one for showing his feelings but you could tell he was very shocked. I had always assumed, because we didn't really know each other, that he didn't care about me. He came to my rescue that night and I will be forever grateful.

Somehow the weekend passed. It felt as if there had been a death in the family! In a strange way there had been. The Jennifer of last week had gone. I was in her place.

First thing Monday morning I got on to the MS Society and Aidan Larkin arranged to call to our house later that day.

We went to see Dr Murphy; he was completely shocked. I had no signs of the disease until my eye went. He was sure it would turn out to be something else. I had known the truth but kept calm for Steve and Keira.

Aidan Larkin called around but he too could not answer my questions. I was so frustrated. I have always thought he mistook my frustration for rudeness. Aidan brought lots of booklets – I am sure I can still recite paragraphs from them, I read them so often. Now all I needed to know was what type of MS I had and would it kill me? Those with a chronic form of the disease can die, though from complications rather than the disease itself. Was I benign/relapsing-remitting/secondary progressive/ primary progressive? Just my bloody luck the disease had stages; it could not be straightforward, not for me!

Steve went back to work. I carried on as normally as possible; when it got too much I purged. Eventually the appointment came for Cork. May the 22nd! It was only the end of February, for Christ's sake. I phoned and begged to be brought forward. There was no chance. I did get my name on a cancellations list with thirty others. I looked into having my MRI privately. Two thousand and sixteen pounds! I had only a couple of hundred.

I began to talk to Steve's dad Ernest, about our situation. Ernest was a straight-talking man. He listened to my fears and tried to assure me I would not suddenly become a disabled person. He had read all there was to read about MS. On hearing about my diagnosis he had requested the books and leaflets from the English MS society. I could not be consoled! My fears were realised every night as I slept. I would see myself in a wheelchair struggling to survive. I did not deserve this! I had suffered enough yet here I was once more with a failing body. My soul had been trapped from birth in this inadequate excuse for a human body. Was I being punished and if so why? I was assured that my eating disorder did not cause my MS, but to be honest I was sure it did.

Every day I had more and more questions to ask, yet no one to answer them. I was lost and in pain. As usual I resorted to my purging to help alleviate that pain. It may sound surreal but when you are as used to that behaviour as I was, it becomes a comfort. It is my secret and I am in control.

We moved from our flat in Salthill to a house in Knocknacarra. Keira needed a garden, as did the dog. I felt like a real person for a few days. I was living in a house with front and back gardens. The flat often reminded me of my cell in London. I would feel trapped and frantic when I was housebound due to the weather or Keira being unwell. I would sit while she slept and feel like the prisoner I once was. The house was big and airy. After two years in the flat it felt like heaven.

I had no sooner planted flowers when I had to leave and go to Cork for my long-awaited MRI scan. We tried to make it into a mini-holiday to take the pressure off. Steve had it all planned out.

"On Saturday we will go to Fota Wildlife Park. Keira will love all the animals and it will take your mind off the scan."

Sure, looking at giraffes will help me forget the scan! Steve was trying his best but all I wanted to do was lie down and die.

"You know, the minute the scan is read my life will change forever. I will be branded 'Jennifer Banks with MS'."

"Don't be silly, Jen. You will always be the same person to me, MS or no MS."

"Steve, I am long enough around to know how everything will change. People will no longer see me – they will only see the MS!"

"Why do you think that? Everyone who knows you will not change towards you."

"When you see a disabled person, what do you see?"

"A disabled person. Why?

"You see the disability first, not the person."

"And what makes you think that will happen to you? It won't – I won't let it."

"If only life were as simple as you see it now. I am a *Disabled Person* now. Jennifer has gone."

"You think too bloody much, you know that?"

"Maybe, but I am right. You will see."

We did the whole weekend-away thing; I hardly remember any of it. I was too stressed and was concentrating on keeping the facade of normality going. Dr Murphy had given me a Valium to take before the scan and I had my James Taylor tape ready. You could bring music to listen to while you're in the machine. I chose music I knew I could get lost in.

On Monday morning I made my way to the hospital. After filling in all the forms, I handed my tape to the nurse. The tape machine was broken! I just gave up at that stage and lay on the table. My head was encased and I began to panic.

Think of the sea rolling on the sand, I began to tell myself, trying desperately to meditate. I was slowly pulled into this round hole and the tears stung my eyes. This was it! Jennifer was dead!

26

The drive from Cork to Galway after the scan was like a funeral procession. With every mile, I knew I was coming closer to losing my identity. The scan would be read and the results sent to my neurologist within days. I was soon to be labelled.

Steve found my way of thinking very hard to accept.

"Why all this talk of death? You're not dying, Jen. Accept it and move on."

"You can't understand what I am feeling. How could I expect you to? After all, I am the one with the MS."

"Well, I am your husband and Keira is your daughter. Don't forget us. We are here for you."

"I know but I have to try and deal with this the best I can. Somehow it seems right to let Jennifer of the past go and start again."

"If it helps, of course I will support you. How do you intend doing it?"

"I don't know yet – all I know is I have to start over."

The books say that a diagnosis of MS is like bereavement. I guess I had latched onto that in some way. I was convinced that letting go of the person I was and beginning again would be the best thing to do.

We went to the hospital the following Friday for my results. I saw Doctor Aaron Brennan. He had a kind and gentle face and I felt confident in his company.

"The good news is, Jennifer, there is no evidence of a tumour. You do, however, have extensive demyelination of the brain and spinal cord."

"I have Multiple Sclerosis then."

"That is what the scan suggests."

"So what do I do now?"

"First I need to book you in for a lumbar puncture, where we can test your spinal fluid for a confirmation of the diagnosis."

"And do you expect to get that confirmation?"

"Based on your MRI results, yes. I am pretty confident of the diagnosis."

"Am I dying?"

"No. MS is a progressive disease and can disable you over time – but you may never reach the more serious stages when complications can develop which sometimes can be fatal. Indeed, you may never have any further symptoms."

While he was talking, for some reason I found myself thinking: 'He would be a good man for Gabrielle.' She had been on her own since separating from her husband three years earlier. I had no idea what Aaron was saying, I was in Looneyland.

We left with a date for my lumbar puncture and as soon as we got in the car the laughter started.

"There is no tumour, Jen. You're not going to die!"

"It's fantastic news – it's only MS and we can cope with that, can't we?"

"Of course we can! You heard him – you may never again have any symptoms. We can go on as normal."

At least Steve had been listening to the doctor. We laughed with the windows open and Eminem blaring on the car stereo. The stress and uncertainty of the past months were being released in our moment of madness.

We went to Honor's house to collect Keira and tell them the news. I was in a state of nervous happiness and knew I would crash later. But for now I was happy.

In bed that night Steve and I planned how we were going to tackle the disease together.

"No matter what happens we'll deal with it. I love you and nothing will ever change that."

"You know me, Steve, always determined, and I won't let the MS get me."

When he slept I kissed his head and went downstairs and cried until my throat hurt. My career was over; I had planned to get back to work once Keira went to Montessori in September. No one would employ me now. I was useless.

Mehmet's words echoed in my ears: 'You are nothing and will always be nothing!'

I held my head in an attempt to drown them out. Now his words haunted me once more. I knew that I could easily break down and had to remain strong. I had survived beatings and years of abuse. I could survive

MS. I washed my face and went to bed, I suddenly realised I had not purged! Or even considered it. Was this it? Had my MS diagnosis cured my bulimia? Maybe some good would come out of this god-awful disease after all.

27

I went in for my lumbar puncture, panicked and checked out. I had seen one done once, when I was in Intensive Care. This woman had come in screaming and roaring – she had to be held down by three people to have hers done. I was not having any of it. In my mind I was fit and healthy and there was no need for any treatment. I was going to get on as before.

I began to experience symptoms during the summer and dealt with them in any way I could. The MS nurse, Mary, was a great support. She herself had the disease and understood me.

"Right now you're in shock and denial. It takes time but you will eventually come to terms with your disease."

"If I accept it then I really do have it. I need that little bit of hope. By not having the lumbar puncture I can't be diagnosed fully. I can hope it's not real."

"You will have to have it eventually. The sooner you start treatment the better."

"When I am ready I will let you know, I promise."

I carried on until October when I began to realise I had no choice but to get treatment.

My neurologist Doctor Moran, whose clinic I was attending but had never met, had shouted at me one day in front of everyone in the waiting room: "If you don't have a lumbar puncture, Mrs Banks, then find another neurologist! I will not treat you!"

I made an official complaint about him.

I used to see Dr Brennan at the clinic and had not crossed paths with this old man before. Dr Brennan was a caring doctor and understood that my panic and denial were all par for the course. I am sure without his and Mary's kindness the journey would have been a hell of a lot harder.

I eventually went into hospital at the end of October and, after arguing that I would be unable to stay still for the test as I would be too afraid, the doctor agreed to sedation. Dr Brennan and another doctor arrived at my room in the mid-afternoon. Steve and I had been sitting quietly waiting. I was given the sedation and the lumbar puncture was done.

When I came round after the sedation, Steve told me I was trying to get Aaron to take my sister Gabrielle on a date! Aaron said he was taken so I asked the other doctor in the room. The drug that was used is called hypnovale and, although I was alert at the time of the test, I have no memory of it ever taking place. Another side effect seems to be losing one's inhibitions. I would never normally try to get my sister a date with my doctor! I was so embarrassed when I heard what I did.

While I was talking to Steve I suddenly felt overwhelmed. I would be diagnosed now and there was nothing I could do about it.

"I have MS, Steve."

"I know but we will cope, I promise."

I cried non-stop for twenty minutes. All the frustrations and uncertainties began to dissolve and I slowly through my tears accepted my fate.

That night I had no sleep. I sat in my hospital bed and planned my new life. I had to let the past be, and move on. I would face whatever this god-awful disease did to me. I had to. I had a family who loved me, and they deserved better than a wife and mother caught up in her past and present problems.

I went home the following day and within hours I was struck with a headache so painful I wanted to die.

I spent three weeks going from the bed to the sofa. As long as I lay flat, my head didn't hurt but even the slightest movement was unbearable. When the headache passed I was fit and well, no symptoms or fatigue – just the odd pains in my hands and legs. My GP was able to give me something to cope with the pain.

I went about planning my future. I spent months trying to work out what I would do. Ernest was having health problems himself but was always willing to listen and advise. At one point he suggested I become an Agony Aunt, using my experience to help others.

"You would be very good at it, you know!"

"What, me? Advise people, after all the mistakes I made in my life?"

"Exactly. You know what it is like."

"Ern, I could never tell people how to live their lives. You have to find out for yourself what to do. I did."

"Not everyone has your strength. You can help them become strong, before they have to learn the hard way as you did."

"Who knows? Maybe someday?"

I had my first Christmas with MS and the world didn't stop turning. My test was positive and the diagnosis recorded. Santa came and was very generous. Keira cried with joy when she saw what was under the tree. I had the perfect Christmas scene in my living room, the grass was white with frost, the room was cosy and warm. I should have been sitting there with a heart filled with joy but I was so very sad. My life as I knew it was over. Would I be capable of coping with what might lie ahead? As usual unanswerable questions! Of all the bloody diseases out there I had been landed with the most confusing of all. But a pattern was hiding there somewhere!

That Christmas morning I decided what to do with myself. I knew I could not begin again with the past hanging over me. I had to move on, let the hurt and pain of my life before Steve go. I had changed and was no longer the weak and fearful person I used to be. I had to get rid of the baggage. I was going to use visualisation and meditation.

I went to the bedroom that night and meditated. I went deeper than I had ever gone before. I asked the universe to take the memories from me. I asked to be empowered. Cleansed for the new person I was about to become. I was starting over as Jennifer Banks. I was no longer Jennifer Grace Ann.

I had saved myself, taken away the pain of the past. I was free, just by visualising the separation of my past and present.

259

I came out of my trance full of strength. I knew my little unit of three would be OK; I had the will to succeed.

My technique helped for a week or so before I realised it had not worked the way I had hoped. You cannot change the past; it is part of you and always will be. I had to find a way to live with mine.

I was always most fearful at bedtime. No matter how hard I tried to push the fear away it always came back. Going to sleep with MS is difficult for me. I never know if I will be OK the following morning. This disease creeps up on you when you least expect it. I had begun to experience severe pain. It was at times torturous. I had learned from my time with Mehmet how to hide from the world outside how I was feeling. I am an expert at hiding pain. Many would faint with the level of pain I can deal with. My mind and body had learned over the years how to cope, so well in fact that I am sure the on-call doctors visiting me during a spasm thought I was making it up. I knew this was an unhealthy way to deal with my situation. I eventually told one of the neurologists how I was feeling. Dr Brennan had moved on, his rotation over, but the new guy, Dr Larkin-Feeney, was also very understanding He prescribed pills for the pain and gave me the letter to begin the treatment for my MS.

On Valentine's Night 2001 I did not receive flowers or chocolate. I was shown how to inject myself! I sat there as the nurse went through the do's and don'ts, wanting to scream at the top of my voice: "*Leave me alone!*" I had been so stupid throughout my life! Trying to have the perfect body had left me with the most imperfect of all. Slowly over the years I had managed to destroy my insides – was this is the price I must pay?

Jesus, did the injection hurt! I let out a scream that almost gave the nurse a heart attack. It turned out the product injected, Rebif (a brand name for a form of Interferon), is thick like syrup. Injecting it at over a hundred mph through the auto-injector is not the most pleasant of feelings. You do over time learn to get on with it.

I was on shot eleven when I began to feel very tired. The morning after my twelfth injection I was incapable of standing for more than a few minutes before my legs gave way. I can't describe the fear I felt, all I can say is that I felt my whole world had collapsed.

Thoughts were running through my head at a frantic pace. What about Keira? How will I manage? Will I ever walk again? What kind of wife/mother/sister/friend will I be? I was a total wreck by the time we reached the hospital.

We met with Mary the MS nurse at the clinic.

"What happened?"

"I woke up like this, Mary. Is this it? Am I now a disabled person for life?"

"Don't worry so much. This will pass in time. You're having a relapse and getting so worked up won't help. You need to try and relax."

"I am so afraid. I want to scream and scream just to relieve the tension in my head."

I was seen by Dr Larkin-Feeney and referred to the seating clinic for a wheelchair! Steve and I drove out to Merlin Hospital in silence. I wondered what he was thinking. I convinced myself he was planning to leave. I have heard stories about women whose husbands left after their wife's diagnosis. Was I about to be one of them?

We were met at the clinic and next thing I knew I was sitting in a wheelchair! I had a full-on panic attack. I was sure I was having a breakdown. The mind is like a thread, Freud said, and at that moment mine was close to breaking. All the years of physical and mental abuse coupled with my self-hatred came crashing in on me. My life was over.

I went home that day with the big black-and-green heap of metal in the boot. I hated the chair and planned to set fire to it. I believe it was my fear of being disabled and hatred of my wheelchair that gave me the determination to walk. I battled day and night until I could stand for at least twenty minutes. I had to rethink my role as a mother and find ways for Keira and me to have fun sitting down. Keira and her dad collected stones on the beach for our garden. Later Keira and I painted them. We made smiley faces, abstract art, and just blobs of colour. The usual works of a three-year-old little girl.

I hated when we went to the beach. I would have to sit alone on the prom and watch others play with my child. One particular day Honor and I took Keira up to the beach. I sat and watched as my sister did all the things I should be doing. I hated Honor at that moment; how dare she have fun with *my* child!

I paid the price for all the self-abuse with my disability and once more Mehmet's words tortured me. I was a 'fat ugly good-for-nothing useless bitch!'. His command of English had often made me laugh in the past. Now I could only feel pain. I was useless.

We had bad days with the wheelchair. I hated being pushed! I was once left in the middle of the road with traffic swerving to avoid me. We had all new pavements along the seafront in Salthill but very few slopes for a chair and none at all at the traffic lights where I was trying to pass! I wrote to the paper in anger and they printed my half-page letter.

Going down the aisles in Dunnes was hell. I had Steve not stopping when I asked him to because he couldn't hear me! In a wheelchair you are facing forward with your back to the pusher – they are also about two foot or more above your head!

But the worst, most unforgivable day with the wheelchair was that of the Salthill Air Show. I sat at the top of the prom waiting for the show to begin, and then I noticed that one by one the family hung their coats, cardigans etc on my chair as well as dropping one on my lap! I was no fecking coatstand and told them to get their stuff off me before I dumped the lot in the sea! Once the show began, other than people's arses the only view I had was fleeting. Indignity and frustration led me to swear so much that day. I was disgusted by people's behaviour. No one moved to allow me to see and when an ignorant passer-by saw me in their way, I received a look of disgust that they had to move around me! I should not be allowed on the prom during such events! I was in the way! And what about all the inconsiderate fools falling over me? They were a risk to me if anything. I never again attended the show in my chair; I was not prepared to become a one-woman army shouting for rights. It was easier to stay away.

As if our lives were not difficult enough at that time, Ernest began to get very unwell during the winter and was hospitalised. The poor man had been battling emphysema for years. Now it began to catch up on him. We loaded the car and set off for Cornwall. I had received a cheque from Ernest a few weeks before; he insisted I went out and bought a computer for Keira and myself. He told me the Internet was the door to my future. I went out and bought the computer as promised. We had hardly set it up when we had to leave and go to Cornwall. I had progressed from the wheelchair to a walking-frame on wheels to a stick, by this time. Steve wanted to bring the stupid chair with us! I objected, ranted and screamed; I did not want it.

We were on the boat when I noticed it in the boot.

"I told you not to bring that bloody thing! Why is it in the car?"

"Just in case we need it."

"I'll throw it overboard if I get the chance. How many times must I tell you? I don't want the chair!"

"And what if something happens in Cornwall? What then?"

"I will crawl if I have to. I won't use it, ever!"

"I'm the one who picks up the pieces, you know!"

"Just leave it. I don't want to talk about it now. We are going to see your dad – the chair doesn't matter."

I was an awful bitch when it came to that stupid wheelchair. I had told Steve he was free to leave, the first time we brought it home. He looked at me and walked out of the room. I heard him whisper under his breath: "What do you think I am?"

I can't imagine living with me then. I was so angry and hurt, I had to lash out. I was up and down by the hour. One minute I was a fighter and the next a wreck.

We eventually arrived in Cornwall after a day on road and sea. Although we had an urgent need to get to the hospital and see Ernest, it was too late. We had to wait until morning. Keira was thrilled to see her nanny; it had been three years since they last saw each other. For Keira it was a first meeting. She would have only been seven months when we were last in Cornwall. But from the age of about two, she used to phone her granddad every chance she got. She knew which button to push on the telephone to get Granddad. I would often come out of the shower, to find her singing away to the telephone. I would take the phone off her to find Ern trying to get her to knock off. He would put the phone down at his end after saying hello to her. Every time he picked it up again he would find her still chatting away. It was all very funny until we received a phone bill for over three hundred pounds!

But now there was an air in the house – I can't explain it; I had felt the same atmosphere when my father died. I knew Ernest was gone from the house never to return.

Walking into the hospital ward we saw a pitiful sight. The strong lively man I remembered was now skin and bone. We spent the day by his side, having our usual extreme conversations when he was up to it. I spoke to him when we were alone about death. Ernest had no beliefs, and was unconcerned about what awaited him. I knew he believed in the spirit world, and we discussed how he could communicate with me after he was gone. For me death is an easy subject. I don't know if it comes from my beliefs or experience, but I have no fear as long as I live long enough to see Keira grow and have children of her own. I will be well pissed off if I die before that! I made Ern promise to tell whoever is on the other side exactly that. I knew Ern was dying, as did he; there was no reason to avoid the subject. In fact Ern preferred to speak openly.

Steve, however, was not coping with the situation. Ernest tried to help Steve understand.

"Ernest, you know Steve won't cope when you're gone?" I said when we were alone.

"He has no choice. He is a grown man with his own family. I have done my time. I cannot change fact. It is better for me to just accept my fate."

"I am not sure I could be so calm. Before Keira was born maybe, but not now."

"It will come to us all. It is only death we can be sure of. You are the next generation and the future is in your hands."

"I don't want to die a cripple."

"And why should you? What you have to do now is re-evaluate your life. Find what you can do, not what you can't."

Ern was like an eccentric philosopher. But he made sense. Here I was worrying about all the things I couldn't do. I needed to find out what I could do and soon before I went nuts.

We spent four days with Ernest. Keira danced and sang for her granddad, and he laughed and cheered when she finished. We have it all on video but don't watch it. It is for Keira to watch and see how much her granddad loved her.

Ernest took me aside on the last day of our trip – he wanted me to say goodbye to Steve for him.

"Tell him I won't see him again and want to say goodbye. But promise not to say a word until you are on the motorway. I know Steve – he will turn round and make a fuss. I hate fuss."

"Don't you think you should have this conversation with him?"

"Now, Jen, you know what he's like. He will fuss and make a scene. We can talk on the phone, when you all get home safely."

"Ern, if you see my parents out there, can you ask them to help me and say hello for me?"

"You can and will help yourself. You're a fighter and I have every faith in you."

"Jesus, I wish I had it myself. I see the MS as another failure. I feel weak and useless. What has life left to offer me? My role now is to raise Keira and guide her as best I can. But what about after she grows up? You know me – I have to keep busy. It will be better for all of us if I am busy."

"Rubbish! You're giving up. I thought you were stronger than that, Jen. Don't disappoint me. I am dying."

We both began to laugh. I knew I had to make something of my life. OK, I could not go back to the hotels, but there had to be something I could do. I just had to find it.

I told Steve on the motorway what Ern said. It broke my heart.

"Why the hell didn't he say this himself?"

"Because you would fuss. He wants to go peacefully and also wants you to be prepared."

"He should have spoken to me. How long has he left?"

"It could be months, weeks or days. Who knows? His emphysema is getting worse. He has read everything about it, even how he will die. You know your dad, Steve; he has to read up on everything. He's not sad or bitter and he wants all of you to feel the same. Phone him tomorrow when we get home. Ask everything you want to know. Don't have any regrets – enjoy what's left."

"You're very like him, you know, always talking sense."

"If only!"

Back home we phoned Ern every day and I set about trying to sort out my life. I spoke to someone who mentioned a distance-learning course for the disabled. There was such a course in Galway, that was all they knew – he had no idea of who was running it or where. I phoned Fás and they had no information about such a course, but a man was on holidays and he might know. Could I phone next week? It was brick wall after brick wall.

I was not going to sit there and die! I got hold of the man at Fás; I don't remember his name only that he gave me a phone number of a college in Galway. I phoned them and they said I had to be registered with Fás before I could apply! What a load of crap! Phone call after phone call and I was back where I started. I went in to Fás, filled in the form and began my search all over again. I eventually ended up in the office of Richard Gibbons. I fitted the course criteria but would have to wait for availability. He would do his best. I am sure Richard could see the desperation on my face. He was a kind man and I knew he would help me; I just had to have patience.

Life at home was moving along. I still felt inadequate.

The pain was now interfering with my sex life. By the end of the day my knees and hips were so painful, sex was the last thing on my mind. Steve seemed to just accept it, and for some reason that annoyed me. I wanted him to shout and scream about the MS and how it had stolen his life and mine! But no, he just got on with things. I felt too that I was missing out on Keira's childhood. She was always with her dad on some adventure or another – I sat at the computer talking to Americans with MS.

I found solace typing away. They understood me. I could spend hours sitting there exchanging my feelings – pretty soon I became addicted to their company. My family seemed uninterested once the initial drama had worn off. It was a case of 'Poor Jennifer has MS'. My situation was no longer exciting or interesting; everyone returned to normal, waiting for the next exciting instalment. As ridiculous as it sounds, my family thrived on drama! I gather it is learned behaviour from the early days; after all, we had almost weekly dramas then, the very same dramas that had so interfered with my childhood. The stupid senseless situations which had been blown out of proportion caused an air of excitement in the house. Here I was, with a very real unending drama but once the initial excitement wore off, so did the interest in my situation.

I had no desire to become a cripple. I had fought back, to the point I was walking with a stick. I was fighting all the way. The toes on my right foot had turned in after the relapse a couple of months before and my leg was weak. I was not accepting anyone's pity. I held my own pity parties late at night. I would sit in the kitchen with my cup of tea and cry. I am not a martyr and have no desire to be. My past was always there to haunt me. As I said, the visualisation technique worked only for a short time. It seemed the right thing to do at the time but you can't just forget something as serious as Multiple Sclerosis. No matter what you do or try to do.

I would cry for the beatings Mehmet gave me, or the babies I had lost. I would cry because I was an invisible child. Mine was a world of pain and regret; I had no idea how the hell I would ever survive it. Where was my miracle? Why was it decreed that I had to suffer? Eventually I would go to bed and sleep. The following morning I would put on my mask, and get on with things. If only people could have seen inside my head even for a minute. It was all a lie. I was not strong, I did not accept my disability, and most of all I was not '*great*'! I was sick of hearing how 'great' I was! I got up, washed, put on make-up just like everyone else. But I was '*great*' just for being able to do it all!

I wish I could tell people it is all flowers and happiness, but a devastating diagnosis like mine is no easy ride. You face demons every minute of every day. The fear is always there; you just learn to cope. I had my bulimia knocking on the door, at every opportunity trying to work its way back into my life. How I managed to keep control is beyond me. I would phone Bodywhys, the Irish Eating Disorders Association, for support on a bad day. On a very bad day I just purged.

I had by this stage in my life walked away from so many counsellors. Suddenly the MS society was offering me a new one!

I went along to meet her and as always we began with my childhood. This counsellor like all the others could not understand how my family had refused to help me. I couldn't be bothered going through all the crap again. I told her straight: "It happened, get over it! Look, the house was full, I was bullied and no one wanted to know, my parents were tired, and the rest had their own lives. I have spent my life in an emotional time-trap of sorts – the child still needs her kiss curls." Needless to say we were not going to have a happy relationship. Why must all counsellors begin with childhood?

I had by now decided that if I never fully accepted my Multiple Sclerosis, then I was in control of my destiny. I still have this little bit of hope in my heart that I don't really have it. Sounds nuts I know but I find that a bit of denial keeps you fighting. It's not right for everyone but works for me.

I must have driven the woman at the MS Society mad with my calls to meet a 'well person' with MS. I was faced with my neighbour, who was in the final clutches of the disease. I needed to meet a person who was well and coping. Eventually I received the call: a woman called Nancy Holland was coming to visit. I opened my door one afternoon to this petite blonde lady with a soft warm smile.

Once she was inside, I realised my saviour had arrived.

"How long have you had MS?" I asked.

"Over twenty years."

"How come you're so well?"

"Not everyone with MS is disabled. I have had my difficult times in the past, but these days I seem to be having more good days than bad."

"I was sure that I was going to end up like a vegetable!"

"Who told you that?"

"Well, no one really, I just presumed it."

"Jennifer, you need to forget all the bad things you have heard and concentrate on yourself. You may never again have any problems with your MS, so stop worrying."

Nancy became a close friend; we spent many a morning sitting drinking tea and smoking. Nancy's visits ended all too quickly every Thursday; I had in her found the hope and strength that had so far eluded me. MS does not always equal disability, but it doesn't matter how often you're told it until you see it for yourself. Most people I meet know someone who knows someone who is very bad indeed! Nancy defied the myth. I now knew someone who has been diagnosed for years and is well – in fact, I now know loads of people who are doing just fine.

I was soon accepted as a distance-learning student, and when my tutor Brendan Doyle came to the house for the first time, I felt I had found another person who brought hope to my door. Brendan was later to become my distance-learning tutor, but he was at this stage only assessing my needs for the course. I had a computer but, in the event that I hadn't, the centre would have allocated one to me for the duration of the course.

I loved Nancy's and Brendan's visits. Between them I managed to regain my confidence and zest for life. Brendan told me recently that when he first visited the house I appeared to be depressed, as if I had given up. It was through him I realised I had only to re-educate myself and find a new path in life. I might no longer be in a position to work in the hotel trade but I had many options awaiting me. I couldn't wait for the course to begin and was delighted that my tutor was such a kind and intelligent man.

I was slowly becoming more mobile, and I began to believe that life with MS was possible.

I went to Gabrielle's daughter Demet's Confirmation on the 13th of May 2001. A party had been planned back at Gabrielle's house and we were all full of merriment. We had no sooner begun the party than Steve's mobile rang.

Ernest had died! I felt my heart stop as Steve told me. We had in a funny sort of way got used to the way things were and expected them to stay the same: Ern was in Bodmin Hospital being cared for until he was well enough to be discharged. Now he was dead.

Steve was heartbroken and I felt so very alone. This man had always been there for me through my troubles. Now he had passed away, I felt I was alone again. I had lost my closest friend. I would bare my soul to him and I felt he never made a judgment. He was my friend and mentor. There would never again be another Ernest in our lives. He was and always will be a one-off.

I had stood at the coffins of both my parents; I would have to face it all over again with Ernest.

Unlike Irish funerals, it takes a week in England to bury your dead. The shock of Ernest's death set off the tremors in my hands and Steve was fearful that the funeral would be too much for me. This, as well as the fact we had a lack of finances, meant Keira and I would have to stay behind. I was saddened and relieved. I did not want to see Ern dead or going to a cremation, something so alien to me. I don't know how I would have reacted. Just the thought of the coffin going behind the curtain gives me the creeps. I imagined myself shouting: *"Stop!"* I would disgrace myself and Steve. It was better I stayed at home.

Honor and I did go to the church with Keira at the same time as Ern's funeral. I had a Mass offered for him. He was an atheist but did keep his options open just in case. I hoped the Mass helped him on his way.

28

I had an appointment to see my neurologist in June. I had a list of questions awaiting answers. I had this almost frantic need to be told I would be OK. I knew full well he could never tell me for sure but I was never going to stop trying to get answers. I went in, sat down and began my quick-fire round.

Dr Larkin-Feeney was on duty that day. He let me rant for a bit then began.

"Mrs Banks –"

"Jennifer, please, the Mrs thing makes me feel ancient."

"OK, Jennifer, you have to try and relax a bit. I know this is a challenging time for you both. I can tell you how MS feeds on stress but I cannot take the stress away – only you can do that."

"You have no idea! I am so afraid. I can't sleep, eat or

think! My life is changing before me and I can't deal with it, I need answers, something to help me cope."

"You know that depression is very common with MS?"

"I am not bloody depressed. I am frightened. I need hope for the future. I need my leg back. My toes turn in and I haven't been able to wear a shoe with a heel for months. Do you have any idea that the loss of what may seem simple to you is devastating to me?"

"I wish I had a magic wand for all my patients – unfortunately until we find a definite cause for MS we can't cure it. All we have is treatment and the chance of delaying progression."

"What type of MS have I?"

"Honestly, with the lack of improvement in your eye after a year I would say you're on the cusp of relapsing-remitting and secondary progressive."

Between the second and third stages of the disease? How could this be happening? I was only beginning to accept my MS bit by bit and now this! I thought it took years to progress between stages?

"Can I stop it progressing further?"

"Your Interferon should help. I believe that if you continue with your treatment, you will see an improvement over time. These things are unfortunately slow to work and take time. We have no instant medication."

"If only you could tell me I can be cured! I leave the clinic feeling defeated every time I come here. I am thirty-six with a four-year-old daughter. I have to be here for her. I have to be well. I keep hoping every day that a cure will come along or that there is one on its way!"

"It is that kind of determination that will keep you going. Believe in your abilities as a mother and wife, stay positive and never give up."

"I think I'm doing that anyway – it's just that I'm seeking a cure as well."

"It could come tomorrow. Who knows?"

"Thanks! Promise you will phone me first when you find it."

I was quiet in the car as we went to pick up Keira. He was right. I had to concentrate on what I could do, not what I couldn't.

Of course all this did nothing to help when I lay in bed later that night, hoping tomorrow would be OK. I hated night. It always brought the bad thoughts. I would have the television on, trying to distract myself. Nothing worked! I did however learn a bit of sign language. Why is it that all the programmes for the deaf are on in the middle of the night?

I would regularly give Steve the out-clause from our marriage. He would get so angry with me.

"For Christ's sake, Jen, is that what you think of me? For better, for worse, in sickness and in health. Remember? I love you whether you can run a marathon or crawl up the stairs. You're my wife and I am here because I love you. The MS is just a pain in the arse but we will deal with it!"

I know that speech off by heart, he said it so many times. If he did leave, I think I would have died! Steve taught me how to love, he made me feel lovable and brought joy to my life.

No man is perfect and Steve has his faults, as do I.

There were times I could kill him. I sent him to the shop once for milk and he came back with dog food! In fact, we have nothing in common! I am outgoing and love to socialise. Steve is shy and quiet. He hates parties, nightclubs and the theatre. We went to see Tommy Tiernan before Christmas and he insisted on sitting at the back, just in case he was picked on! It's always the same. I would be delighted to have a laugh and be picked on, and Steve runs a mile. It is this that binds our marriage. We love to laugh. All arguments end in laughter. One of us will make a ridiculous statement, the other cracks up and that's the end of it. But as much as I must get on Steve's nerves (occasionally), he is forever trying to wind me up! He has this ridiculous game for the car: he talks about *Grange Hill,* the TV programme, for ages, then you have to answer questions. If you get one wrong he starts all over again! He drove Aisling and Demet, Gabrielle's daughters, demented with the game for months, phoning them up on spec to ask questions! If he had a brain he would be dangerous! But I love him.

Steve's humour made waiting for the doctor easy. When I would spasm in the early hours he would ask who Gripper Stebson was? Answer: the bully in Grange Hill. As time went on and the spasms increased it was not so easy to laugh, but I have to say I found Steve's behaviour funny as always. He would be hopping around the house, frustrated at being unable to help, but his attempts at being helpful were something else.

"Can I do anything? Will I rub your leg?"

"If you touch my leg I will kill you!"

"There must be something I can do?"

"Keep an eye out for the doctor!"

He would stand watching the road, and I would try so hard not to laugh at the concentration on his face as he did it. It must be so awful to watch someone you love in pain. Thankfully this was something I did not have to do with Steve. He was of course 'dying' if he had a headache or his colds were always full-blown flu but after a few hours of sympathy he would miraculously recover from death's door. He remained strong and kept us going during the bad days, but on a good day his constant fussing was a pain in the arse.

It did take time for us to find the laughter, after my diagnosis and the loss of Ernest. I had a permanent cloud of confusion hanging over me and Steve was in shock. You never imagine that you will come back from these situations. I would tell myself that in my thirty-six years I had survived an eating disorder, marital abuse, serious illness and the loss of Shauna. The MS was just another stone that landed at my feet. So why the hell was I not coping? Was this one problem too far?

We were hitting rock bottom financially. Steve had stopped working in order to look after me, and the rent and day-to-day living expenses were killing us. Our savings ran out in six weeks, as we were too proud at first to go to Social Welfare. I remember when the Welfare Officer came to the house and asked how we were living. She was shocked when I replied: "Our savings." Keira was in Montessori, which was twenty-five pounds a week, not much when you can afford it, but we couldn't. Eventually we had no choice but to ask the St Vincent de Paul for help. I felt so ashamed every Monday night when these people came to my home with shopping vouchers. They were so kind and always wanted to help us but deep down I was ashamed. But what else can a person do? Until our Social Welfare was sorted out we had only the minimum payment of one hundred and twenty-six pounds a week to live on. With twenty-five going to Montessori and forty to rent, trying to keep on top of bills was killing us, never mind shopping for food! Whatever we had or did not have at the time, Keira's needs were always put first. Steve and I could live on cheap food but a growing child needed nutrition.

We were not in receipt of full rent allowance as we had a three-bedroom house! Jesus, if I knew when I rented it I would have a diagnosis of MS, then I would have got a two-bedroom! The State makes no allowances for unexpected illness. Our Welfare Officer was wonderful, and did everything she could to help; but even she could do nothing about the extra bedroom. It was to be the worst year of our lives, more so than the diagnosis itself.

Not knowing if you will be well enough tomorrow just to cook a meal is horrifying. But not having the food to cook with was unimaginable. We somehow managed to keep going. Steve had to do everything: clean, look after Keira and worst of all care for me! I got up every day no matter how bad the pain or fatigue, showered, dressed and put on my make-up. Then it was a crawl downstairs to spend the day on the sofa, unless I had to crawl upstairs again to use the loo. Steve was always by my side. In time we received our full welfare allowance, after months of living on just one hundred and twenty-six pounds a week. We were able to thank the Vincent de Paul for all their help and say goodbye. I made a promise to myself that I would in some way repay their kindness and I have over the years since donated any extra cash I may have at Christmas to them.

Steve was then on Carer's Allowance and allowed to work a few hours each week. In an attempt to get him back to work, he paid my sister Honor to come in a couple of days a week and sit with me, or do some housework. We also wanted to have a holiday, so extra money was vital. We had never had a honeymoon and decided to go to Euro Disney for a few days. Keira was mermaid-mad and the house was bursting with all the pictures she had drawn of Ariel, *The Little Mermaid*.

Keira was very well adjusted and other than the odd question (usually "Are you going to die from your MS?") it seemed not to affect her. Still aware of how I had been so fearful when my own mother got sick, I had decided to answer all her questions honestly in a language she understood, the simpler the better. Her attention span for explanations was short so I used simple and to the point answers: "No, Keira, Mummy is not going to die. You don't die from MS."

That was all she needed to hear.

We went on like this until I was finally allocated a place in the National Learning Network; just knowing that I was off Disability Allowance was wonderful. Nothing had really changed only that I received my money directly from the centre and no longer had a book with the words 'Disability Allowance' staring me in the face. Yet it was so liberating. I was no longer a number and need not use the term Disability Allowance on any of the numerous forms that came my way.

I began after a few months of waiting to study for my ECDL (European Computer Driving Licence) – a certificate in computer skills recognised throughout Europe – through the National Learning Network. Brendan had been to the house several times, setting up equipment, but this was the start of the course.

At my first in-centre meeting I came into contact with other disabled people. It may sound strange but I had never had contact with people with disabilities before. I am sure if we all ask ourselves honestly how many people with disabilities we know, the answer will likely be that unless a friend or family member is disabled our contact is minimal. I realised I was now part of a separate group in society. I had joined this group purely by the label of disability itself! I was now Jennifer Banks PWD – 'Person With Disability'. Well, I was not going to accept any more labels in my life and found my fellow students, all with acquired disabilities, felt the same. My excitement at ditching the Disability payment book was soon halted when I learned I was and always would be labelled 'disabled'.

I had a chip on my shoulder and my mind was filled with all the labels I had lived with during my short life. I was desperately trying to make sense of my existence. The bulimia was lurking in the background as usual, and I often thought of taking the easy way out and punishing myself with the purging! But I had a family now and this changed everything. I could no longer afford to inflict pain on myself without hurting them. I loved the monthly meetings with Brendan and especially when we met outside the house with all the other students on the programme. I made new friends, Gráinne and Maggie in particular. We got along and helped each other out along the way. I used to meet up quite a bit with Maggie and we talked about setting up a business when the course was finished. I was dead excited and talked for many hours with Steve about how it would work. He was behind me one hundred per cent.

Every day I became more and more confused and my life was spiralling out of control. Then I came into contact with Paddy Doyle, author of *The God Squad*, his life story of neglect and abuse at the hands of a religious order in one of their Dublin orphanages. Paddy was so over the top and his views on disability brought me laughter and sense. He has a way of making his point and taught me I was as valuable a person now as ever. I was not society's cast-off – in fact I was society's teacher.

I was suffering with pain from my MS on a daily basis and I discussed using cannabis with Paddy. He was all for it – in fact, he has publicly stated this in the past. He had a couple of plants and I arranged to pick one up from him. What I found in Paddy was a very unique man living his life with a chronic disability, who still had a sense of humour.

Steve and I had been saving to get to Disney to meet Ariel, *The Little Mermaid*. All the months of saving were worth it to see the child's face when she saw Ariel come around the corner in the Disney parade. Keira cried with happiness and the three of us followed the parade's route with Keira shouting, *"Ariel, I love you!"* all the way. The woman kept blowing back kisses and that day Keira was the happiest child alive. The four days in Disney cost as much as a two-week holiday but for that moment when Keira saw Ariel it was well worth it.

We went to Paddy's house on the way back through Dublin and picked up my cannabis plant, which was named Rodney.

Paddy allowed me to see life beyond my MS. If I had any 'buts' he would simply say: "Fuck them!" and go straight to the point. I told him about my life and we talked for hours about the good things, which with age made the bad seem unimportant.

I had begun a cycle of good days and bad days with my MS and I could talk to people about my problems, real people who understood like Nancy, Brendan and Paddy.

So why was I still so caught up in my past?

My friend Anita kept telling me to stop trying to be accepted by my family! I had no idea I was trying to be accepted. I just thought I was trying to be a good sister.

I still remember waking up as a child at home in my parents' house on a Sunday morning and under my bed would be a bottle of Club orange – Gabrielle always brought a bottle home to me after her night out. I can still feel the excitement of looking under the bed – the bottle would be hidden but I knew it would be there. One Sunday morning there was none. I don't know why or when the custom stopped, what I do remember is looking for years and finding nothing. I could have been no more than five or six when the custom was broken. Maybe Gabrielle had found herself a boyfriend or something, who knows? But as a child I took it as rejection. I am a sensitive creature, always have been and it is this nature that has kept me trapped in these memories.

We had a field in our street owned by the farmer down the road. Lolo for some reason promised to buy me a pony. Christ knows how it came about but I can remember telling every one of my friends I was getting a pony. I planned to keep it in the field opposite our house and ride it every day. Daddy would build it a shed and Mammy would give me scraps to feed it. The whole thing was planned out but my friends, after a few months of me telling them about my pony, began to call me a liar! I had no idea it was a joke and cried when I found out. I had been told I was a liar and it stuck! I eventually stopped talking about myself or my dreams for fear of being laughed at. I only just recently spoke to Dolores about this. She said she was a teenager playing with her little sister and the fantasy story was all part of it. I like a fool told people. It was all harmless fun, so why was I destroyed by it? From the kiss curl to the orange, then the bully and the pony, little by little it all became the key to my self-hatred. And now I was having to deal with it all over again.

Steve had no idea how bad I was feeling. I kept it all hidden. I was after all an expert at hiding things, especially my feelings. While I was desperately trying to cope with my insane existence, I was forever caught up in my past. I had to find answers to my questions before I could move on. I asked each member of the family in turn why I felt so unloved? Did I do something terrible, so terrible I can't remember? But their answers were always the same. When I was a child everyone had their own lives to live. I just happened to be there. As for the lack of visits and interaction during my time with Mehmet, they were fearful of him! He was five foot eight, no Tyson, and certainly no danger to anyone except me. For the life of me I can't understand it. I am sure I went to Mehmet as a cry for help. When it went unanswered, I was trapped in a controlling and abusive relationship. Yes, I promised to leave him, all abused women do. The difficulty is actually doing it! I know I should have left and gone home when the abuse began, but my self-hatred had me tied up in knots for years. I made my parents, brothers and sisters the focus of my anger. To admit that I was the person with the problem would have meant accepting I hated myself – it was easier to believe that they hated me. Of course I also had Battered Woman Syndrome thrown into the mix; I was so fearful and under his control. I had the desire to leave every day and I think in the back of my mind I knew I would one day, hence the 'run' account. I could only find freedom for myself. Having the family telling me to leave would not have worked no matter how many times they tried.

I am told so often by my sisters how privileged a life I led as a child What was missing was the nurture. Gifts, money and good schools don't make up for not being able to tell people you're hurting. Because I didn't talk about it, then it never happened. I was being relentlessly bullied by another child and worst of all an adult. Between them, I was convinced that I was unlovable! As I said, my pain manifested itself in self-abuse and loss of self-worth. All the others remember is the things I received and they can't see what was missing. My mother was unwell. For a few weeks, I was sure it was my fault and when she recovered I was sure she blamed me! I truly believe she had a minor haemorrhage in her brain when I was eight – it explains everything – what I perceived as my mam no longer loving me was most likely as a result of her haemorrhage. I now fully understand what happened between my mother and me and I know a lot of it is my fault. But I can't help feeling that I had no place in the family. I will run to my family's aid, yet even when there is no more Mehmet I must ask to be aided myself. Lolo said it is because I appear to be so strong no one knows when I need help. This is most probably true but I wish that just once I didn't have to ask for assistance. If I say I am having a bad day, then I am. I find if I try to talk about being upset or unwell the subject is passed over. I may have to go to the grave with my questions unanswered and it is this that causes me most pain.

I did, however, get a shocking answer from Dolores recently.

"Maybe we didn't believe you were sick."

"How could you not believe me? Doctors don't cut people up for no reason."

"At the time so much was going on. You were with Mehmet and I know I would not phone the hospital and ask you to bring me home perfume if I thought you were really sick."

"But all the surgery I had! How could anyone think I was not in trouble?"

"I can't answer. I honestly don't remember."

"Lolo, I am shocked. Mammy spoke to my consultant. She must have told everyone what was wrong with me surely. And didn't I come home after the surgery, scars and all?"

"I swear, Jennifer, I can't remember. I honestly think we didn't take you seriously."

I am staring at the words 'we didn't believe you were sick' trying to make sense of it all, but I can't. I am nearing the point of giving up wanting answers. I do not want to die having wasted my time and energy chasing the past.

29

While I was studying, a woman called Julie Grace arrived at my home in Monalee Heights one evening. She arrived during chaos. Keira had just had a tantrum. Gabrielle and Demet had called to the house and Keira didn't want Demet to go. Gabrielle's girls, Aisling and Demet, were the closest thing to sisters Keira had. She loved and adored them both and they loved her too. Family days out always included Aisling and Demet. We were like one big family. When I was diagnosed, Gabrielle and Honor were there as I had been there for them during their difficult times. I never left Honor's side when Daddy was ill and after his death when all the family were divided. It seemed right that they were there for me. I actually felt secure for a time.

Julie had come to discuss adapting a house for me; I was going to have my own home once more. I cried with joy that night as I dreamed of us living in a house where I didn't have to crawl up the stairs to go to the bathroom. My dream house was to take a few years but at least I knew it was there. I met with architects, discussed my needs and I can honestly say I was always treated with respect and understanding by everyone I met on Galway City Council.

I was doing well in college and meeting new people all the time. I had begun to live again; I could see a future for myself. I had ambitions to go back to work and earn my own money once more. I hated being dependent. I wanted to shop without conscience, buy perfume when I needed it and not just at Christmas and birthdays. I wanted to buy Keira all the beautiful clothes I saw in the shops.

It was a phone call from Paddy that would change my life.

"I have just had a paper come into me. Rehab are going to set up a media company for people with disabilities. It's perfect for you."

"Sure, I haven't a clue about media, Paddy. How could I get a job in it? Plus I live in Galway, remember, and Rehab is in Dublin."

"Will yeh just listen to me? The idea is you can work from home as a journalist, and study media at the same time."

"I have no experience."

"Fill in the application form and take a chance."

"And how am I supposed to work for a Dublin organisation? I have no idea if I can walk tomorrow let alone work."

"For Christ's sake, woman, will you just fill in the application? It's on the web. Then phone a woman called Katriona. She is the project manager."

"I'll give it a go."

I spoke to Katriona Kerrigan and we arranged an

interview for a place on the programme for a couple of weeks later. I didn't think too much about the position and got on with my exams here in Galway. I had, with the help of Steve and my friends, begun to live again. I made plans for the future and found, with Nancy's kindness and understanding and Paddy's encouragement, I was talking about setting up my own business. Brendan and Richard Gibbons arranged a meeting for me with a small business advisor. I attended with my friend Maggie and we discussed the possibilities of setting up the Daisy Chain, a home-based service for small businesses. We were going to offer typing and account services. It looked as if it could work. And I was looking forward to getting back into employment once more.

The date for my interview with Katriona arrived and I travelled to Dublin with the few articles I had recently written. I really had no expectations as I had no official training in the media. I had studied communications as part of my Hotel and Catering course; otherwise I had nothing to offer.

I was more excited about meeting up with Paddy as I had a couple of little cannabis plants to pass on. 'Rodney', the cannabis plant I had received from Paddy, had turned out to be female and was throwing out babies at an amazing rate; he was kicking himself over that one. My bathroom was like a greenhouse. Steve was rather enjoying cultivating the plants. I made tea rather than smoke it; I felt that by smoking the cannabis I would be breaking the law and the tea is not illegal. Stupid, I know, but the mother in me was always aware. The tea worked a treat. I found that I was off all but my basic medication for the six months since I had started drinking it.

However, I was half dead with a chest infection when Katriona phoned me to give me the news that I would be one of the ten people chosen to work for Mediability, a pilot production company staffed with ten disabled people. The poor girl did not get the most excited reaction until I realised I would have the chance of working as a journalist, something I would never have considered before.

The only downside would be being away from Steve and Keira a couple of nights a month. I had never left Keira since the day she was born; I did my housework when she was a baby with her strapped to my chest in a sling. Now I would have to stay away! When I spoke to my now five-year-old daughter a solution was found as to how she would be a good girl for Daddy. Blackmail. I would have to return with a present for her.

"Mum, I promise if you bring me back a nice present, then I will be good for Daddy, promise!"

"What kind of present are we talking about here? A book maybe?"

"Well, I was thinking a doll."

"A doll, every time Mummy stays away?"

"Well, you see, then I won't cry because I will be excited waiting for my present!"

"So every time Mummy goes away, you get a doll and then you won't cry and you'll be good for Daddy?"

"Yes."

I went to see Maggie to explain about the job in Dublin. She was fine about it all, thank God, but I was terrified that I was letting her down. After that it was all systems go and I made my first trip to Dublin.

I felt insecure about meeting my colleagues. I was about to embark on an adventure of sorts, and there were nine new people to meet. All the way up on the train I was worrying. "What if they don't like me, or worse what if I'm not good enough?" I was introduced to the production manager/tutor Dan Dwyer and sitting around the conference table were eight new faces (someone decided it was not for them), probably all as nervous as me, but none of us showed it. We spent the two days together, all treading lightly. I asked a lot of questions about how we were going to study and work. The programme was designed so that our work could be put forward as assessments along the way and all exams would be taken when Dan felt you were ready.

I was now a working journalist, with Mediability. I even had business cards. I had a long hill to climb but over time I began to get to know my colleagues. Sinéad first, then Mary and Gillian. We were all spread across the country but we began talking on the phone to each other. I found that I suddenly had a whole new circle of friends to go with the programme. When asked about myself I found the truth hard to tell. How unbelievable my life has been! Surely they would think I was exaggerating? I decided the past was not of interest to anyone. I need only talk about the present.

I will never forget my first article. I was covering the anti-war protest in Galway. I joined the march with my minidisc recorder and walked straight up to Michael D Higgins TD. The buzz of walking alongside him recording an interview was wonderful. I went home, typed up my article, and for the first time in years felt a little importance. I was born for this! I knew it! Me a journalist! Who would ever have thought it? It's like this side of me was waiting to come out. I loved giving out business cards and hated studying. Returning to the books sixteen years after you thought you had closed them for the last time is daunting but worth it. I had during the year post-diagnosis thought that I would never work again. I was wrong. There was a place in society for me and I was flying high.

During one of my trips to Dublin, Paddy had a gift for me: Doyle's Liniment. He had been working on ways of using cannabis without ingesting it. His new liniment had been designed to be rubbed on the point of pain. I was sceptical but took the jar home and agreed to give it a try.

"When trying something new and untested my motto is you should always try it out on the husband first," I said. "If he survives then give it a go yourself!"

I told Steve to rub some on his hand and nothing happened. A couple of hours later, Steve was off his head. Everything from the tap to curtains were the most hilarious things he had ever seen. We decided to head up to bed for fear that this superhuman fearless man might hurt himself. After I had crawled up a few steps Steve lost it and sat on the hall floor laughing.

"Do that again, Jen! Go on! It's so funny!"

"Do what?"

"Crawl up a step. If you could only see yourself! It's mad!"

"Ha ha, pass me up the phone, will you?"

The phone on its short journey from hall to the middle of the stairs where I was sitting became a *Star Trek* phaser, as Steve sang Bowie's *Ground Control* and called occupants into the thing.

I phoned Paddy. It was after midnight but I wanted to relay the news.

"Paddy, I have here a man off his head after a rub of the liniment!"

"You're joking! It's not that strong!"

"Oh, I'm not joking. I think we may have found a way to sell the liniment on the open market to more than just pain sufferers!"

Steve was calling "Hi, Paddy!" as I tried to talk. He was completely out of control but the funniest thing I had ever seen in my life. There, lying on the hall floor, was my husband professing his unadulterated love to the dog!

"I love you, Tash! You're gorgeous, you know that? You're the best girl ever, little Tashy-washy!"

Steve had lost the plot. I sat laughing and talking to Paddy for over an hour. Then he asked how much cream Steve had used.

"Steve, how much of the liniment did you rub into your hands?"

"What?"

"You know, the jar of cream Paddy gave me – how much did you use?"

"I don't know? A little bit, I think."

"Can you get the jar for me?"

"Paddy, how much cannabis was in the cream?"

"A fair bit. I ground it to powder first."

"Here he comes now – Steve, can I have the jar?"

"Only for a kiss!"

"Come on, Steve, please!"

"No, you have to kiss me first!"

"Fine. You'll give it to me then, promise?"

"Maybe."

It took not only a kiss but a few promises before I got the jar off him.

"It's nearly all gone, Paddy! How much was in it?

"It was full. The feckin' ejeit won't come down for days! You have a great night ahead of you!"

"Steve, why did you use so much?"

"You said to rub it in like hand cream!"

"I meant use a little bit, not three quarters of it!"

"It's all your fault, you didn't explain it, so there!"

I was now the mother of two! Steve in his state of euphoria had regressed to a five-year-old but it was the best night's fun I'd had in years. I laughed, Paddy and his wife in Dublin laughed and most of all Steve laughed. We talked well into the night and planned a patent and worldwide launch for Doyle's Liniment. I gave the stuff a try with the little bit I had left and although I had some relief, I thankfully remained sane unlike Steve.

It seems insane that two cripples on either side of the country were trying to develop a way to relieve their pain by any means. Without a research laboratory or highly trained staff, Doyle's Liniment was born. The only problem is we would have needed to break the law in order to supply it. Paddy had also begun to 'murder' the baby plants I gave him! Not only was he now killing off my babies, he was destroying the stock needed for the liniment! He just didn't have the green fingers for the job – to be honest, I don't think Paddy was or ever will be the gardening type.

Our lives had taken a turn soon after I went back to work. There was more laughter than tears those days and I was so tired after studying I fell asleep without worry. I still had MS and I had to live with that fact but I now had a way out. Keira moved from Montessori to school, still untouched by the disease. My concerns over ruining her life were unfounded. I answered all her questions in simple short explanations – she usually walked away before I finished. Our kids are stronger than we give them credit for and I will always be thankful that my disease struck while Keira was so young. It was just the way things were as far as she was concerned.

Meanwhile, poor Dan Dwyer was close to pulling out his hair with my punctuation! He would regularly ask me to take time and correct these mistakes. He went so far as to bring me a book and I in one of my silly moods sent him an email:

Dear Dan,

Thank you for bringing the book. As you can see it's working already.

Bye for now.

I don't know if he got the humour or not but it was obvious that I had not lost the devilment from my schooldays. Dan was always trying to encourage me and told me often I had the ability to write. I began sending things into the local media only to be rejected time and again. The only writing anyone accepted from me was disability-focused. I would first get angry, then start again. I began aiming high. I asked those in power for interviews as well as celebrities. One man whom I found very approachable and willing to help was Eddie Hobbs, the financial advisor and presenter of *Rip Off Republic*. I interviewed him at half time during a rugby match. Eddie was funny and very interested in what I was doing. It was his interview that opened the lines of communication for me with other media publications.

Healthwise I was still battling the daily annoyance of MS. I went so far as to break the 'No Steroids For Me' rule I had lived by for five years. The treatment is all well and good but the last thing you give a person with an eating disorder is a drug that makes them fat! Never mind the 'Does my bum look big?' question, I was sure I weighed half a ton.

Steve was constantly bombarded with statements such as:

"Steve?"

"Yeah?"

"Do I look really fat in this?"

"For feck sake, will you give it up, Jen!"

"Give what up?"

"The 'Am I fat?' shit! I'm sick of it! You don't look any different now than you did going into hospital."

"So I've always been this big? Why didn't you tell me?"

"Will you just shut up? You're not fat. You're Jennifer, the woman I love and am married to. You are also the mother of Keira so don't go messing with dieting. She needs you well."

I would move on for a few days then the Fat Demon would reappear! I began telling myself I was perfect as I was, that we are not all the same. I drove Steve nuts and myself a little dotty until I just started laughing.

You know what? I couldn't care less what society thinks of me any more. I have my super five-mile-an-hour scooter for the bad days and dare anyone block my path! I have knocked over displays in Penny's as they were in my way and driven over the toes of unmoving people who stand in my way in the street. There is something sadistically entertaining about having the five-miles-an-hour as your feet. You should see people's faces when I ram my way through the clothes displays looking for a bra. If anyone asks, well, they should be further apart in the first place. And anyone who ignores my horn for more than a few minutes will be moved – if they complain, well, I didn't see them, did I? If I am invisible, then so are they.

We moved into our house and the freedom of adaptation is wonderful. I no longer crawl to the bathroom; I have an adapted one downstairs and another one upstairs with my supercharged one-mile-an-hour stairlift. Not a good idea when one is in the throes of passion to use the lift – the moment is lost during the journey. By step four you run out of things to say! Best stay wherever you are at the time.

Dan and Katriona were always encouraging me. I wanted to work in radio and had created a programme format for *Talkback With Banks*. I was never once told that my idea was silly or not good enough. I was taken to RTÉ and NearFM to record sample shows. The bug bit me. Dan guided me through my exams and always told me I was capable of doing whatever I wanted. "Just learn to punctuate!" Now what good would I be if I didn't keep people busy with my punctuation? I write as I think and speak. I seldom come up for air when talking and that is how I write – sure, Dan would be bored if it were not for me and my mistakes.

I loved working with Mediability and still do. I always have some idea I am working on, no matter how daft! The girls and I have a great laugh when we meet up. Gillian sadly left and was replaced by Jim. We promised to keep in touch but as with all such promises time passes and then you feel too embarrassed to call, as it's been so long. Jim is one of the most intelligent people I have ever met. His wit is dry like my father's was and he can keep you talking well into the night.

So I was really enjoying my life and then out of nowhere the MS struck me down again and I was off to see the neurologist once more. I don't do follow-ups and only appear when something is wrong.

"Can you cure me yet?"

"No, Mrs Banks, we are still trying. What can I do for you?"

"Well, I'm weak, my speech is slurred and the walk is bad."

"A bit of everything then?"

"Why not? It seems to me MS is incapable of just one little problem at a time. It's lots of little ones. To be honest, I just don't have the time for this."

He just looked at me. I don't think doctors are used to people stating they lack the time for their disease.

I was a new patient for my neurologist. He was not long after taking up his post and here I was telling him I could only spare enough time for a quick fix!

"Maybe you are doing too much – MS has to be managed."

"Right now managing my MS is not on my agenda. You can't tell me how long I will be fit and well for, so I have to do what I can now."

"You can still do this but you must learn to manage your disease."

"How?"

"Pace yourself, work while you can and rest when you need it."

"I need to be normal. I have to be there for the sleepy

glow every morning when I go to call Keira for school. I can't miss out on the soft tired hugs and the time with my child."

"Jennifer, we can only offer you advice – it is up to you to take it."

I could feel Steve getting frustrated beside me.

"Will you just listen to the man, Jen, please? I'm demented with her, doctor. She never listens and then when something happens she wonders why."

"I can offer a pill which has been effective with fatigue, but it is up to you to care for yourself properly. You have to rest. This is imperative with fatigue. I am not saying never get out of bed – I am talking about power naps. Take twenty minutes when you're feeling tired; have a cup of tea, sleep, whatever. It will help you work more effectively rather than running yourself into the ground and then wondering why."

"I feel like a failure when I give in. It's as if I have to fight all the time."

"Feeling this way is normal and in the long run the fight in you will help, but you just have to recharge."

"I am here too, you know, Jen. It's not all up to you – you have to let me help."

Now that was rich coming from Steve. His idea of help is always good-natured but he has a habit of doing the wrong thing at the wrong time. He takes Tasha out or hoovers the car, truly believing he's helping. Then the ironing is backed up or the dinner needs cooking. He can't see it and I don't want to tell him what to do, as I would be nagging him all the time. I decided to employ Honor to do the ironing and my pal Nicola helps in the house. I was lucky enough two years ago to be given the services of a personal assistant to help with the things I have difficulty with. Hoovering wears me out and I have a tendency to drop things. I also do not drive any more for fear of losing control of the car. I was terrified of having a spasm with my foot on the accelerator and decided it was best to stay off the road altogether. Nicola takes me out to do the shopping or pay the bills, whatever needs doing. I can't imagine not having the service. I am a bit of a perfectionist when it comes to doing stuff; my hotel background has me haunted when it comes to cooking and cleaning. If you don't use the right product or cook at the right temperature, then you're doing it wrong. So I insist on doing the cooking but I am getting better and not overdoing it. I just don't do boredom or illness very well.

The whole independent woman movement is great but asking for help or saying no is difficult. My healthy friends think my refusal to go out at night is boring. They just don't get it! I have spent so much of my time explaining why I have no energy for nights out that the calls have stopped. The days I find myself wanting to tell the world to feck off, I play the hostess and shut up. I sit and listen to people complain about life when I am in so much pain fainting sounds good. I don't tell people my woes very often because I am so used to either being talked over or going unheard it seems pointless. I have found comfort in my friends with disabilities. We understand each other. I phone Sinéad or Mary and we can tell each other how we feel without the concern of sounding boring. I am not going to change people or society so I don't try. What's the point? You have to be a little bit selfish about these things and only concern yourself with yourself. A lesson I have learned only in the past couple of years, much to Steve's delight. I am more involved with Bodywhys, the Irish Eating Disorders Association, than disability. The thought of people going through what I did is horrendous.

I will always have my bulimia demon but if you're caught early you won't have to. With counselling and support, eating disorders can be overcome. If I had asked for help all those years ago I might never had gone on to develop bulimia or anorexia. If you have the slightest suspicion that you or a friend/family member may have a problem with food, give Bodywhys a call and seek help. I lived the life I did and there is no going back. At times it was really horrible and the bullies are always there. As Paddy would say, "Feck them!"

My GP Dr Dan Murphy has been a tower of strength to both Steve and me. The man would spend as much time as you needed with you. You are never rushed and your opinions are listened to. I am not sure if I could have come this far were it not for Dr Murphy's support for me and the family.

Meeting and marrying Steve was my true saving grace. I have learned to allow and accept love. I see him in ways as my mother's gift to me. Fate and the universe conspired to have this drunken woman laughing on the radio while Steve was turning the dial. How strange that it was her anniversary that day! I found this loving caring man who claims to look like a boxer! That, ladies, is a lie! He is adorable and cuddly. Life became what it was meant to be when we met; we have survived what would make many run to the divorce courts. And still we are in love and this makes life bearable.

I have with his love and my determination managed to learn to live with the past. I am in recovery from my eating disorder and the extra pounds are no longer a life-and-death matter. I live with my MS on a day-to-day basis and have recently had it confirmed that I do have the relapsing-remitting form of the disease and am no longer on the cusp between it and the next stage.

I guess the medication has pulled me back a bit. I am happy and content.

Epilogue

Steve booked a sitting with a local photographer for the three of us, on our wedding anniversary. I bought Keira the cutest of dresses and Steve and me new clothes. I wanted the photographs to reveal our family, the unit of three. Keira and I had our hair done and when I put her dress on she looked so huggable. I was so proud of my family! These photographs were going to be perfect. We piled into the car and Steve stopped at the church.

"I just want to light a candle."

"What for?"

He was studying to become a Catholic. I thought maybe it had gone to his head. I never encouraged or discouraged him to do this. He said that after his dad died it felt right. Olan, our priest, was young and honest. I found his effect on me brought me back to Mass. I loved to hear him speak as it was truly from the heart. I spoke to him a little about my life and he didn't do the 'God is the answer' bit. He said the answer was in me, the strength was always there to recover, I just had to find it.

We got out of the car and Steve took a bag from the boot.

"What's that"?

"Nothing."

"What are you up to, Steve? Are you getting baptised or something?"

"I could be."

"Well, tell me then. Don't keep me in suspense."

You could tell he was getting a bit nervous and I was sure we were at the church for his baptism. Why he had kept it a secret I didn't know but he was very shy if he didn't know people and doing it this way was probably the right thing for him – but why keep it from me?

We walked up the hill and Olan met us at the door.

Then Steve asked for my wedding ring,

"What are you at, Steve?"

"Just be patient, will you?"

Now Steve should know better than to ask me to be patient! I am the most impatient person you will find. I often feel like getting out and pushing the train on my way to Dublin – if Irish Rail ran on time it would be dangerous – we would be so confused on arrival that at least ten minutes would be lost trying to get over the shock!

Steve was over in the corner with Keira, hiding something and still asking for my ring!

I gave it to him and then I realised what was happening.

"Jen, I love you, MS or no MS. You said I probably wouldn't have married you if I had known. Well, now I do and I want you to do me the honour of being my wife, again."

Saving Grace

I looked and saw Keira holding the silk ivory cushion that had held our rings the day I married Steve. I kept it safe in a box as it was so very precious and special to me and now my own daughter was holding it.

"Of course, I will. I love you so much it hurts sometimes!"

"Even when I'm being stupid?"

"Even when you're being stupid, and most of all when you make me laugh."

The doors to the church were opened and waiting on the altar were Anita and my family.

Steve and I had tears in our eyes as Christy Moore's 'The Sailor' began to play.

I walked behind my beautiful child and held the hand of the man I loved as I stepped slowly towards the altar. My life and everything that happened to me was worth it for this moment.

THE END

List of Organisations

BODYWHYS EATING DISORDERS ASSOCIATION
Helpline: lo call 1890 200 444 or
email: info@bodywhys.ie

BodywhysConnect:
bodywhysConnect@bodywhys.ie

MULTIPLE SCLEROSIS SOCIETY
MS Helpline 1850 233 233
Website: www.ms-society.ie

WOMEN'S AID
Everton House
47 Old Cabra Road
Dublin 7

National Freephone Helpline 1800 341 900
Phone: (01) 868 4721
Fax: (01) 868 4722
Email: info@womensaid.ie
Website: www.womensaid.ie

RAPE CRISIS NETWORK IRELAND
2nd Floor
The Halls,
Quay Street,
Galway

Telephone: 091 563676
Fax: 091 563677
Email: rcni@eircom.net
Website: www.rcni.ie

Direct to your home!

If you enjoyed this book why not
visit our website:

www.poolbeg.com

and get another book delivered straight to
your home or to a friend's home!

www.poolbeg.com

All orders are despatched within 24 hours.